ENGLISH MEDIEVAL FURNITURE AND WOODWORK

AMIENS CATHL

ROYAL ARCHITECTURAL MUSEUM
BEDFORD LEMERE & Co.'s, 147, Strand, W.C.
(ARCHITECTURAL PHOTOGRAPHERS & PUBLISHERS)

16

ENGLISH MEDIEVAL FURNITURE AND WOODWORK

by Charles Tracy

VICTORIA AND ALBERT MUSEUM

PHOTOGRAPHIC CREDITS
Royal Commission on the Historical Monuments of
England (FIGS 1, 4, 6, 17-22, 28, 29, 31, 32, 34-35, 38, 41-43, 46,
48, 55, 57, 58); Dr Carolyn Malone (FIG 2); Miss Anna
Hulbert (FIG 3); Conway Library, Courtauld Institute of
Art (FIGS 5, 12, 16, 24, 53); Dr Charles Tracy (FIGS 7, 8, 10, 26,
27, 30, 33, 36, 37, 39, 44, 47, 49, 51, 56); Metropolitan
Museum of Art, New York, All Rights Reserved, (FIG 9);
Provost and Scholars, King's College, Cambridge, (FIG 11);
Canon Maudie H. Ridgway (FIGS 13, 14, 45, 52); Salisbury
Cathedral (FIG 15); Victoria and Albert Museum (FIGS 23,
25); B. T. Batsford Ltd (FIG 40); Country Life (FIG 50); Mr
Reece Winstone (FIG 54).

Designed by Tim Harvey
Printed by Napier, Jones Limited

COVER
Background decoration, rood screen panels from St. John
Maddermarket, Norwich (CAT. 100 & 101)

FRONTISPIECE
Royal Architectural Museum. Plaster casts of misericords
from Amiens Cathedral and miscellaneous woodwork
fragments from English churches. From original
photograph by Bedford Lemere (Conway Library,
Courtauld Institute of Art).

CONTENTS

Foreword   vii
Acknowledgments   ix
List of Plates   xi
List of Figures in Text   xvi
Introduction   xix

I. ECCLESIASTICAL

Details of Roofs   30-50
Doors   51-52
Reredos   53-54
Misericords   55-69
Parts of stall canopies   70-74
Screens and Screen Panels   75-95
Stall- and Bench-Ends   96-120
Portion of Cupboard   121-123
Portion of Font Cover   124
Portions of a Shrine   125

II. DOMESTIC

STRUCTURAL WOODWORK AND FITTINGS

Corner Posts   145-147
Windows   148-149
Doors and Doorways   150-158
Roofs and Ceilings   159-160
Screen   161
Panels and Panelling   162-171

FURNITURE

Chests and Boxes   172-184
Cupboards   185-191
Tables   192-193
Chair   194
Forms and Stools   195-200
Miscellaneous Posts   201-205

Collation of Museum numbers and catalogue entries 206-207
Abbreviations and Select Bibliography   208-215
Index of places   216

FOREWORD

Early English furniture and woodwork has not been a popular field of study in recent years. The materials tend to be scattered and fragmentary, provenances are usually lost, and even when woodwork is preserved *in situ* it is often mutilated and undocumented. A further discouragement lies in the high quality of the many pioneering works published in the first part of this century. The original version of this catalogue, which appeared in 1923, occupies a secure if minor position in their ranks. Its author, H. Clifford Smith, then an Assistant Keeper in the Department of Woodwork, acknowledged the help of two outside experts, F.E. Howard, whose *English Church Woodwork* of 1917 is the classic account, and F.C. Eeles, the first secretary of the Council for Care of Churches.

In 1984 the Museum again turned to an outside expert for the revision and recasting of the 1923 catalogue. It was fortunate to secure the services of Dr Charles Tracy, who has contributed much to a renaissance of interest in the subject. Particularly valuable aspects of this new version are the introduction, which constitutes a first extended account of the historiography of English medieval woodwork, and the very full bibliography. However, the entries are the thing, and in many cases Dr Tracy has shed new light on objects which were neglected and enigmatic. If some have defeated his detective zeal, this is no criticism of his perseverance in the Museum, from store-rooms to library, and with bicycle and camera in the field. Mention should also be made of the valuable contribution of Ken Jackson, who took the many new photographs required for this catalogue.

In the 1923 preface it was stated that: 'It is not the policy of the Museum to encourage the removal of treasures from churches or other public buildings but to rescue and preserve such as have lost their proper homes, so far as very limited financial resources make it possible'. The Museum's policy remains unchanged, and so, alas, does the state of its finances. Its collection of medieval woodwork has thus remained remarkably static since the 1920s. Dr Tracy's catalogue should however demonstrate that the Museum is still fully committed to the study and 'proper safeguarding of what has survived the iconoclasm of former generations'.

Simon Jervis
Deputy Keeper
Department of Furniture and Interior Design

ACKNOWLEDGMENTS

My thanks are due to Dr Clive Wainwright, Dr Richard Fawcett, Mr Francis Cheetham, Miss Anna Hulbert and other colleagues whose advice I have sought in connection with this project. I am grateful to the staff of the museum's Department of Furniture and Interior Design and the administration at Osterley Park for their assistance. The University of London's Computer Centre generously provided a computer-readable version of the previous catalogue. The Westfield College Computer Unit allowed me to use their equipment to type my text. My thanks also to Mrs Constance Hill and Mr Geoffrey Fisher of the Conway Library, Courtauld Institute of Art, for all their help. Most importantly, I am grateful to Mr Simon Jervis, who invited me to prepare this new edition, for his support and his corrective insights.

COLOUR PLATES

1
St Katherine's Hospital-by-the-Tower.
View of choir from the east. Watercolour
drawing by John Carter. 1780 (Port of
London Authority Collection – Museum of
London).

2
Boss from St Alban's Abbey with lion
gnawing a bone
W.51-1914 (cat. 17).

3
Four panels from a reredos
W.34 to W.34c-1912 (cat. 62-65).

4
Parclose screen panel from Great Barton,
Suffolk with painted Annunciation
W.50-1921 (cat. 94).

5
Panel from St John Maddermarket,
Norwich with St Agatha and St William of
Norwich
24-1894 (cat. 101)

6
Panel from St John Maddermarket,
Norwich with St Leonard and St Agnes
23-1894 (cat. 100).

7
Four panels from a rood screen with
Adoration of the Magi, West Country
W.54-1928 (cat. 102).

8
Two painted panels from Tatterford,
Norfolk
271-1906 (cat. 103).

BLACK AND WHITE PLATES

ECCLESIASTICAL

BOSSES

1 a-d
Bosses from Berrynarbor Church, Devon
(cat. 1)
126, 127, 128-1908 & circ. 1222-1926

2 a, b & c
Bosses of lioness, cleric and female head
from former bishop's palace, Exeter
(cat. 5-9)
119, 123 & 124-1865

3
Foliage boss from Bishop's Palace, Exeter
(cat. 6)
120-1865

4
Foliage boss from Bishop's Palace, Exeter
(cat. 7)
121-1865

5
Boss with winged lion (cat. 14)
W.34-1924

6
Boss with winged ox (cat. 15)
W.35-1924

7
Boss from St Alban's Abbey with hawthorn
foliage (cat. 18)
W.51D-1914

8
Boss from St Alban's Abbey with 'stiff-leaf'
foliage (cat. 20)
W.51E-1914

9
Boss from St Alban's Abbey with maple
foliage (cat. 22)
W.51I-1914

10
Boss from St Alban's Abbey with oak
foliage (cat. 23)
W.51J-1914

11 a & b
Scottish bosses with floral decoration and
voluted 'trefoil leaf' (cat. 30-31)
W.107 & 108-1926

12
Boss with head of a bishop (cat. 37)
W.10-1931

13 a, b & c
Corbel of angels holding a harp, lute, and
lute or gittern (cat. 38-40)
W.21, 22 & 23-1911

14
Angel corbel from Louth church (cat. 42)
A.1-1910

15
Corbel of angel holding a shield (cat. 45)
W.26-1921

16
Figure pilaster (cat. 48)
W.7-1928

DOORS

17 a & b
Two doors from St Mary, Beverley
(cat. 57-58)
W.5 & W.5A-1921

MISERICORDS

18
Misericord from Wells Cathedral with
crouching man (cat. 66)
W.48-1912

19
Foliage misericord from Lincoln Cathedral
(cat. 67)
W.104-1924

20
Misericord with crouching man (cat. 68)
W.25-1924

21
Threshing misericord (cat. 69)
W.7-1921

22
Stooking misericord (cat. 70)
W.8-1921

23
Eagle misericord (cat. 71)
W.52-1921

24
Carting the corn misericord (cat. 72)
W.53-1921

25
Misericord from St Nicholas, King's Lynn,
with gorged and chained leopard (cat. 73)
W.6-1921

26
Misericord from St Nicholas, King's Lynn,
with ecclesiastic at prayer (cat. 74)
W.9-1921

27
Misericord from St Nicholas, King's Lynn,
with falcon and rabbit (cat. 75)
W.10-1921

28
Misericord from St Nicholas, King's Lynn,
with stag and hounds (cat. 76)
W.11-1921

29
Misericord from St Nicholas, King's Lynn,
with crouching lion (cat. 77)
W.12-1921

30
Misericord from St Nicholas, King's Lynn,
with master-carpenter (cat. 78)
W.54-1921

31
Misericord from Blagdon, Somerset with
three cloaked heads (cat. 79)
W.4-1948

32
Misericord from Blagdon, Somerset with
vine leaves and fruit (cat. 80)
W.5-1948

33
Assumption of the Virgin misericord
(cat. 87)
377-1890

PARTS OF STALL CANOPIES

34
Canopy arch from St Katherine's-by-the-
Tower (cat. 89)
W.21-1921

35
Boss from the Winchester Cathedral choir-
stalls (cat. 90)
236-1897

36
Arcading fragment possibly from a stall
backing (cat. 93)
W.3-1928

SCREENS AND SCREEN PANELS

37
Portion of rood screen from Tilbrook,
Cambridgeshire (cat. 95)
W.82-1921

38
Panel with sunk quatrefoils from Lincoln
Cathedral. (cat. 96)
W.102-1924

39
Two pairs of screen doors from a Devon
church (cat. 97 & 98)
118 & 118A-1865

40
Screen panelling from West Stow, Suffolk
(cat. 104)
W.149-1921

41
Frieze of cornice from Zeal Monachorum,
Devon (cat. 109)
W.412-1922

42
Figure of an angel. East Anglia (cat. 121)
W.19-1916

43
Tracery head from a Somerset church
(cat. 123)
511-1893

44
Tracery head from a Suffolk church
(cat. 126)
W.151-1921

45
Tracery head from a Suffolk church
(cat. 127)
W.413-1922

46
Tracery head from Suffolk (cat. 128)
W.23-1921

47
Tracery heads from a Suffolk church
(cat. 131)
W.150A-1921

48
Tracery panel from a Suffolk church
(cat. 134)
W.6-1924

49
Tracery panel from a Suffolk church
(cat. 135)
W.7-1924

50
Tracery panel from a Suffolk church
(cat. 138)
W.5-1924

51
Tracery panel from a Suffolk church
(cat. 139)
W.11-1924

52
Panel carved with sacred monogram
(cat. 149)
W.10-1936

53
Arcaded panel (cat. 150)
Circ. 99-120

54
Last Judgement panel (cat. 157)
W.63-1938

STALL AND BENCH-ENDS

55
Portion of a stall-end from St Nicholas,
King's Lynn, displaying two-masted ship
(cat. 158)
W.16-1921

56
Portion of a stall-end from St Nicholas,
King's Lynn, displaying single-masted ship
(cat. 159)
W.6-1916

57
Stall- or bench-end from St Nicholas, King's
Lynn, with hooded figure (cat. 160)
W.3-1916

58
Fragment of stall- or bench-end from St
Nicholas, King's Lynn, displaying gorged
yale (cat. 161)
W.5-1916

59
Fragment of a stall- or bench-end from St
Nicholas, King's Lynn, displaying a
cockatrice (cat. 162)
W.7-1916

60
Fragment of a stall- or bench-end from St
Nicholas, King's Lynn, displaying a
mantichora (cat. 163)
W.8-1916

61
Fragment of a bench-end from St
Nicholas, King's Lynn, in the form of a semi-
detached column surrounded by a winged
figure (cat. 164)
W.9-1916

62
Finial of a choir-stall with the arms of the
town of King's Lynn (cat. 167)
W.11-1916

63
Bench- or stall-end from St Nicholas, King's
Lynn (cat. 168)
W.14-1921

64
Bench-end from St Nicholas, King's Lynn,
with grotesque animal with hoofed feet.
Detail (cat. 174)
W.56-1921

65
Stall standard from St Nicholas, King's Lynn
(cat. 178)
W.60-1921

66 a & b
Two bench-ends from a Suffolk church
(cat. 184 & 185)
W.94 & W.95-1911

67
Upper portion of a stall desk-end with
carving of St George and the Dragon
(cat 186)
299-1907

68
Bench-end from Norfolk or Suffolk with
human mask poppy-head (cat. 189)
W.76-1924

69
Bench-end from Norfolk or Suffolk with
seated figure on elbow buttress. Detail
(cat. 190)
W.77-1924

70
Bench-end from Great Tew (cat. 195)
W.91-1911

71
Bench-end from North Somerset (cat. 199)
W.29-1923

72 a & b
Two bench-ends from Devon or East
Cornwall (cat. 201 & 202)
W.17 & W.18-1913

73 a, b & c
Portions of bench-ends from Balderton,
Notts (cat. 215-217)
W.8, W.9 & W.10-1958

PORTION OF CUPBOARD

74 a & b
Two doors from a cupboard with carved
figures of the Virgin and St John the
Evangelist (cat. 234 & 235)
W.5 & W.6-1911

PORTION OF FONT COVER

75
Finial of font cover (cat. 236)
W.27-1921

DOMESTIC

CORNER-POSTS

76
Corner-post, known as 'Finney's Post'
(cat. 239)
W.42-1920

77
Corbel-bracket or corner-post with figure
of woodwose (cat. 240)
W.6-1928

78 a & b
Two corner-posts from Bury St Edmund's
with heraldic decoration (cat. 241 & 242)
W.6 & W.7-1909

WINDOWS

79
Window-frame from a house in Hadleigh,
Essex (cat. 245)
W.59-1913

DOORS AND DOORWAYS

80
Arch or cartway, and doorway and door
from the Church Farm, Clare, Suffolk
(cat. 247 & 248)
726 & 727-1902

81
Doorway and door from Key Street,
Ipswich (cat. 249)
A.25-1913

82
Linenfold door in two parts (cat. 251)
W.68-1916

83
Linenfold door from Lavenham, Suffolk
(cat. 252)
W.57-1913

84
Linenfold door probably from Norwich
(cat. 253)
368-1905

85
Square-headed arcaded door (cat. 254)
754-1895

ROOFS AND CEILINGS

86
Portions of beams from Suffolk or Norfolk
(cat. 260)
W.28 to 37 and W.62 1921

87
Piece of cornice or cresting from Sutton
Place, Guildford (cat. 262)
1969-1900

SCREEN

88
Hall screen from Brightleigh, Devon. Detail
(cat. 266)
W.1-1946

PANELS AND PANELLING

89
Panel fragment with Royal Arms of
England (cat. 268)
W.2-1928

90
Royal Arms of England supported by
winged angels (cat. 269)
W.34-1927

91
Linenfold panelling possibly from the back
of a settle (cat. 270)
539-1892

92
Five panels of linenfold ornament (cat. 271)
661-1904

93
Linenfold panel (cat. 277)
W.18-1930

94
Linenfold panel with spiral ends (cat. 276)
W.42-1921

95
Parchemin panel with rose, vine, thistle and
hop foliage (cat. 278)
W.66-1921

96
Parchemin panel with grapes and leaves
(cat. 279)
W.153-1921

97
Linenfold panel with oak leaves and pine
cones (cat. 281)
W.39-1928

98
Parchemin panel with foliated cusps and
initials 'G' and 'T' (cat. 282)
W.48-1914

99
Parchemin panel with Lombardic initials
'M' and 'T' (cat. 284)
W.49-1914

100
Flamboyant panels from Sutton Place,
Guildford (cat. 286)
1974 & 1974A-1900

101
Linenfold panel with leaves and fruit
(cat. 294)
Circ. 578-1925

CHESTS

101
Linenfold panel with leaves and fruit
(cat. 294)
W.30-1926

102
Hutch chest with chip-carved decoration
(cat. 296)
W. 158-1921

103
Hutch chest from a Surrey church (cat. 297)
W.158-1921

104
Hutch chest from Great Bedwyn Church,
Wilts (cat. 298)
W.22-1920

105
Ark chest (cat. 299)
W.21-1913

106
Carved chest-front with scenes from the
Life of the Virgin (cat. 300)
W.15-1920

107 a & b
The 'Fares' chest, front and back view
(cat. 301)
W.20-1913

108
Boarded chest with geometric carving from
East Anglia (cat. 302)
W.428-1922

109
Boarded chest carved with cusped ogee
arches (cat. 303)
W.98-1922

110
Boarded chest carved with three rows of
decoration (cat. 304)
W.69-1916

111
Framed chest with linenfold panelling
(cat. 305)
W.85-1921

112
Framed chest with linenfold panelling
(cat. 312)
W.28-1930

113
Framed chest with 'parchemin' panelling
(cat. 313)
W.11-1938

CUPBOARDS

114 a, b & c
Desk and cupboard for books. General
view and details (cat. 314)
143-1898

115
Livery cupboard (cat. 315)
721-1908

116
Two panels from a cupboard (cat. 316)
W.37 & 37A-1924

117
A pair of panels from a cupboard front
(cat. 317)
W.36-1913

118
Buffet door (cat. 318)
1973-1900

TABLES

119
Side-table or low buffet (cat. 319)
W.47-1910

120
Table and form from Broadway, Somerset
(320 & 324)
262 & 263-1908

CHAIR

121
Arm-chair (cat. 321)
W.39-1920

FORMS AND STOOLS

122
Form from Barningham Hall, Suffolk (cat.
322)
W.67-1921

123
Form with ogee-shaped framing (cat. 323)
W.78-1924

124
Form from Broadway, Somerset (cat. 324)
263-1908

125
Stool with pierced framing (cat. 325)
W.95-1921

126
Stool with incised and carved framing
(cat. 326)
W.65-1916

127
Model of a bench or moveable settle
(cat. 327)
A.4-1911

128
Back of a wall bench or fixed settle (cat. 328)
W.25-1923

MISCELLANEOUS POSTS

129
Set of four posts (cat. 330)
W.18-1911

130
Three decorated posts (cat. 331-33)
W.22 to W.22B-1913

131
Two decorated posts (on outside) (cat. 334)
W.40 & 40A-1914

131
Decorated post (in centre) (cat. 335)
W.41-1914

132
Portion of posts (cat. 336)
W.33 & 33A-1929

LIST OF FIGURES

1
V & A Museum
St. Nicholas, King's Lynn, Woodwork
collection (part).

2
Wells Cathedral
Upper spandrel in nave, north side, bay 7-5.
East. Detail.

3
Exeter Cathedral
East bay of nave. Lioness boss.

4
Salisbury Cathedral
Effigy of Bishop Bingham, d.1247. Detail.

5
Hereford Cathedral
Bishop Cantelupe's shrine. Spandrel.

6
St Wendreda, March, Cambs
Angel from base of hammer beam roof.

7
St James, Louth, Lincolnshire
Angel figure from dismantled 15th century
nave roof.

8
Westminster Abbey
Figure of Gabriel from Annunciation group
in Henry V chantry.

9
Metropolitan Museum of Art, New York
(The Cloisters Coll.)
Alabaster figure of St Fiacre.

10
St Botolph, Boston, Lincolnshire
West door.

11
King's College, Cambridge
Charter of 1446. Detail of the two Houses of
Parliament.

12
Wells Cathedral
'Flight of Alexander' misericord.

13
St Cuthbert, Darlington, Yorkshire
Reclining man misericord.

14
Gloucester Cathedral
'Green Man' misericord.

15
Salisbury Cathedral
Detail from 'Creation of Eve' scene in
chapter house arcade sculpture.

16
Hereford Cathedral
Reclining Old Testament personage
misericord.

17
Worcester Cathedral
Misericord with corn reaping.

18
Norwich Cathedral
Blemya misericord supporter.

19
All Hallows, Wellingborough,
Northamptonshire
Misericord showing master-carpenter at
work.

20
St George, Stowlangtoft, Suffolk
Falcon with rabbit misericord.

21
St Martin, Worle, Somerset
Misericord with vine foliage and fruit.

22
St Martin, Worle, Somerset
Misericord with two heads in a cloak.

23
V & A Museum
Alabaster panel of 'Assumption of Virgin'.
(Acq. No. A. 62-1946).

24
Winchester Cathedral
Vaulting of choir-stall canopies. Detail.

25
V & A Museum
Jesse Cope. Detail.
(Acq. No. 175-1889).

26
All Saints, Tilbrook, Cambridgeshire
Section of roodscreen (from J.K. Colling,
Gothic Ornaments, London, 1850, II, Pl. 66).

27
Lincoln Cathedral
Choir desk front. Detail.

28
St Michael, Barton Turf, Norfolk
Figure of St Apollonia from rood-screen.

29
St Peter, Buckland-in-the-Moor, Devon
Adoration of the Magi panel from rood-
screen.

30
Whalley Abbey, Lancashire
Choir-stalls. Detail.

31
Sherborne Abbey, Dorset
Last Judgement misericord.

32
St George's Chapel, Windsor
Last Judgement panel on desk front.

33
Private Collection
Coronation of the Virgin panel.

34
St Mary, Bishop's Lydeard, Somerset
Bench-end with ship.

35
Wiggenhall St German's, Norfolk
Bench-end with yale.

36
St Mary, Bury St Edmund's, Suffolk
Yale on bench-end.

37
St Botolph, Boston
Yale on choir-stalls.

38
St Mary, Stonham Aspall, Suffolk
Bench-end with cockatrice.

39
Lincoln Cathedral
Stall desk-end.

40
St George, Stowlangtoft, Suffolk
Bench-ends.

41
St Gregory, Norwich
Wall painting of St George. Reproduction
in watercolours by E.C. LeGrice.

42
St Mary, Wilby, Suffolk
Bench-end with axially facing figure.

43
St Nicholas, Rattlesden, Suffolk
Human mask poppy-head.

44
Salisbury Cathedral
Choir stall-end.

45
St Ives Church, Cornwall
Screen fragment. Detail.

46
St Giles, Balderton, Nottinghamshire
Bench-end.

47
Westminster Abbey
Figure of Virgin from Annunciation group
in Henry V chantry.

48
St Helen, Wheathampstead, Hertfordshire
Font cover.

49
Holy Trinity, Wensley, N. Yorkshire
Possible wooden shrine and alms box.

50
Paycocke's House, Coggeshall, Essex
Archway and door

51
Luton Museum (Bagshawe Collection)
Panel with simple chamfered ornament.

52
St Michael, Stanton Harcourt, Oxon
Rood screen. Detail.

53
St Mary, Thornham Parva, Suffolk
Retable. Detail.

54
All Saints, Wraxall, Avon
Tomb of Sir Edmund Gorges. Detail.

55
St Mary, Stoke D'Abernon, Surrey
Chip-carved 13th century chest.

56 a & b
Lincoln Cathedral
Lion's mask motif on stall elbow and
misericord.

57
Muchelney Abbey, Somerset
Measured drawing of settle in abbot's
parlour of former abbey (Stratton &
Garratt).

58
St Botolph, Trunch, Norfolk
Font and cover.

INTRODUCTION

It will be seen from this catalogue that the Victoria and Albert Museum's collection of medieval furniture and woodwork is biased in favour of ecclesiastical examples. This fact reflects the situation throughout Northern Europe where, in general, medieval churches have tended to escape the ravages of decay, war, fashion, and political revolution more lightly than secular buildings.

Compared to most other northern European countries the survival in England of medieval ecclesiastical interior furnishing in wood is astonishingly comprehensive. For example, it can be said that in twelve of the seventeen English pre-Reformation secular and monastic cathedral choirs most of the medieval wooden furnishings have been preserved. At Salisbury, Norwich, Winchester, Lincoln and Carlisle the original sets of choir-stalls are still intact. At Exeter the complete set of misericords from the thirteenth-century choir-stalls has survived, together with important components of Bishop Stapledon's magnificent early fourteenth-century oak choir furniture – the remarkable bishop's throne, a fragment of the choir-stalls,[1] the choir and other parclose screens,[2] and the eagle lectern, now in St Thomas' church, Exeter.[3] On the other hand there was a wholesale destruction of interior wooden furnishings at the Dissolution of the Monasteries. The greater churches had all been fitted with more or less elaborate wooden furniture. The vast majority of this is lost to us, a pathetically small number of *disjecta membra* surviving either in part of the same building, if it was fortunate enough to be converted into a parish church, or in the new owner's local church or house. Of the five Benedictine and Augustinian monasteries saved by Henry VIII by being converted into cathedrals, the magnificent complete sets of choir-stalls at Gloucester and Chester survive intact. Collegiate establishments fared better. The important sets of furniture in the north country churches at Ripon, Beverley and Manchester survived. Unfortunately, only one set of choir-stalls in the Gothic style from the medieval royal chapels has come down to us, that of the fifteenth-century St George's Chapel, Windsor. Several smaller collegiate churches retain some or all of their wooden fittings, especially those dating from the fifteenth century. There are complete sets of choir-stalls of the fourteenth century at Etchingham and Arundel, both in Sussex, and at Nantwich, Cheshire. From the thirteenth century there are the choir-stalls in the chapel of St Mary's Hospital, Chichester. Much of the stallwork of the mid 1360s from another English medieval hospice belonging to the royal foundation of St Katherine's Hospital-by-the-Tower is preserved (COL.PL.1). Moreover at New College, Oxford, the fitted interior of a medieval academic collegiate chapel can be seen, albeit somewhat rearranged.

But it is at the level of the parish church that England's surviving stock of medieval furniture and woodwork is most noticeably richer than it is on the Continent. This country has suffered a destructive Reformation and a civil war but we have not been invaded by a foreign army since 1066 nor have we experienced a secular revolution. Of course the Cromwells, Thomas and Oliver, have much to answer for. It is possible to point to specific losses, such as the famous historiated choir-stalls at Peterborough Abbey or the carved biblical panels above the seats at Winchester Cathedral, both victims of Civil War iconoclasm. But the destruction in England never approached the scale and thoroughness of that suffered in France and the Netherlands following the French Revolution. It is in the diversity of the surviving structural woodwork and furniture of our parish churches that England's comparatively good fortune manifests itself. The roll-call of surviving categories of woodwork indicates the sheer range of the medieval carpenter's activity – open roofs, timber vaults, timber porches, roof bosses and corbels, rood screens, rood lofts, rood canopies, parclose screens, porches, doors, font covers, benches, choir-stalls, bishop's thrones, pulpits, pyx covers, banner staves and lockers, effigies, cupboards and hutches, Easter sepulchres, altars, reredoses, altar ceilours, sedilia, lecterns, chests, and alms boxes.

There is very little evidence of any genuine antiquarian concern on the part of the church authorities in England before the proselytizing of Pugin, Ruskin and Morris in the middle of the nineteenth century. In 1775 the original thirteenth-century choir-stalls at Westminster Abbey were ejected by dean and chapter. At about the same time William Essex expelled the twelfth-century pulpitum at Ely in order to facilitate the removal of the fourteenth-century choir-stalls from their original placement under the octagon into the presbytery. Also in this period James Wyatt cleared away the pulpitum at Salisbury Cathedral so as to provide an unobstructed view from west to east. Pugin's famous pro-medieval polemics such as *Details of Antient Timber Houses* of 1836, where the wanton destruction of vernacular medieval architecture is ridiculed, or his *A Treatise on Chancel Screens and Rood Lofts* of 1851, where the French counterpart of the notorious East Anglian Civil-War vandal William Dowsing falls victim to his own machinations, helped to inspire a serious historicist movement amongst architects. Unfortunately, however, the demands of the ecclesiologists were at odds with this new respect for archaeology. The destruction of medieval furniture, such as the return stalls at Chichester Cathedral, continued. On the other hand, in the second half of the nineteenth century this renewed interest in medieval art produced the significant benefit of many sensitive and high quality campaigns of restoration of wooden furniture, for instance at Salisbury and Rochester cathedrals.[4]

The neo-Goths of the 1840s and '50s thirsted for examples of genuine medieval joinery, particularly secular furniture of the fifteenth century. Before the foundation of the South Kensington Museum the simplest way to study Gothic art was to acquire it yourself. This was the practice of many of the first generation of neo-Gothic Victorian architects. The most notable exponent was the younger Pugin whose personal collection was unrivalled, not to mention the acquisitions he made in a professional capacity for his enthusiastic clients. Another avid collector was the architect L.N. Cottingham (1789-1846). He crammed his house in Waterloo Bridge Road, Lambeth, with a horde of specimens of English and Continental Gothic art. The entire contents, arranged into nearly one thousand five hundred lots, was disposed of at auction after his death. The sale catalogue, however, survives.[5] In it the auctioneers emphasise that the collection had been built up over a period of thirty-five years 'for the purpose of professional study and comprises Original Specimens, Models, Casts, Furniture and Decorations, from the most perfect remains of each epoch and style, arranged in apartments of appropriate character, thus forming a complete practical illustration to the Study of English Architecture, Ecclesiastical and Domestic, from the period of the Norman Invasion to the Close of the reign of Queen Elizabeth'. The following list of the more important items of Continental and English woodwork speaks volumes for contemporary taste during the formative years of the Gothic Revival.[6]

English
Panelled ceiling from Crosby Hall.
A portion of the upper part of stalls from Magdalene College, Oxford.
Twenty-three linenfold panels from Layer Marney, Essex.
Five panels from the wooden ceiling of the chancel of St Mary's, Bury St Edmund's, Suffolk, with angels playing musical instruments.
A stall end from Henry VII's Chapel, Westminster Abbey.
Ten misericords from Stratford-on-Avon parish church.

Continental
Flemish altar-screen, about 1490 (Formerly in the possession of the Duke of Orleans, Phillipe Egalité).
Fragments of choir-stall ends probably from St Mary in Capitol, Cologne. Thirteenth century.
Figures from a fifteenth-century Flemish Crucifixion group.
Fifteenth-century cradle.

The formation of private collections like these must have stimulated the desire for a permanent national collection of the 'Applied Arts'. The South Kensington Museum was established in the 1850s,[7] as much to provide the best examples of earlier art for students to copy as to present them for the enjoyment of the public. It was part of a school of design as well as a museum. The fragmentary nature of dismantled medieval woodwork was not a disqualification to acquisition. At an early stage a large collection of mainly Continental panels, many of high sculptural quality, was acquired. The seriousness of purpose behind the Victorian obsession with historical decorative ornament is underscored by the methodical way in which the new museum set about making plaster facsimiles of English medieval art.

The view of a museum as primarily a study collection was shared by the Royal Architectural Museum, founded in 1851 (FRONTISPIECE). This institution developed in parallel to the V&A until it was effectively merged with the larger body in 1910. Doubtless the V&A would have wanted to form a collection of medieval secular furniture of the type represented in Henry Shaw's, *Ancient Furniture*, published in 1837. However, genuine specimens were, of course, extemely rare and there were plenty of fakes on the market. A notable example of a misunderstood specimen, if not strictly speaking a counterfeit, is the so-called 'Prince Arthur's Cupboard'.[8] This was acquired by the museum in 1912. Although accepted in the literature as an important historical piece its authenticity is questionable to say the least. It has been omitted from this edition of the catalogue.

The acquisitions of medieval woodwork and furniture by the museum during the first fifty years of its existence are numerically relatively unimportant. The most active period for acquisition was the third decade of the twentieth century. This phenomenon may be partly accidental but must also reflect the popularising influence of antiquaries such as William St. John Hope, Francis Bond, Fred Crossley, Frank Howard, J.C.Cox, Alfred Harvey, Aymer Vallance, Fred Roe, Alfred Maskell, George Druce, Edward Prior and Arthur Gardner. These pioneers of modern scholarship had, in effect, put the subject firmly on the English cultural map in both its ecclesiastical and secular manifestations. From our perspective the first two decades of the twentieth century saw a time when traditionally educated bicycle and railway-borne historian/archaeologists ceased to concentrate their attention on the individual artefact and its ornament, and developed instead a broader multi-disciplinary methodology, which embraced a more rigorous and scientific approach to archaeology and to liturgical, social, ecclesiastical, political and technological history.

The objects in the V&A collection were acquired either by purchase or gift. The most important source was the Royal Architectural Museum. This institution, which originally had its home in Canon Row, Westminster, and later moved to Tufton Street, was set up in 1851 as the nucleus of a 'National Museum of Architectural Art'. Subsequently its collection was exhibited for some years at the South Kensington Museum. However, the strain of cohabiting with an institution of such a different hue led the Architectural Museum to revert to the use of their own premises. The problem in our national artistic life that this institution was designed to solve was succinctly stated by George Gilbert Scott in his *Guide* to the collection: 'that, though architects themselves may travel from place to place, and study the ornamentation of each great production of the architecture of the middle ages or of classic antiquity, such is not the case with those art workmen to whose hands must be committed the actual execution of the more artistic parts of our modern works'.[9] The idea was, therefore, to provide a place for artisans to repair to in their free time to study the minutiae of architectural ornament. The objects of the South Kensington Museum, in catering for a much wider and less specialised clientéle, were seen to be quite different. The first printed catalogue of the Royal Architectural Museum was published in 1855. When the museum was closed its contents were dispersed. The V&A acquired a large number of plaster casts of architectural material. Such items were the bread and butter of Victorian art collections.

Of some forty private collections from which the V&A benefitted it is possible to mention only a few. One of major international importance from which items of various kinds were purchased was formed in France during the second half of the nineteenth century by Abbé Peyre.[10] Many English private collections were probably accumulated over generations by unremarkable landed gentry families. Such were the Clarkes of Bridwell, near Tiverton in North Devon.[11] They had lived in the same place since the early seventeenth century intermarrying with other local families and, no doubt, acquiring property and chattels along the way. In 1913 a collection of 'Early English Oak Furniture, Woodwork, Armour and Arms, Stained Glass, Pottery, Coins and Medals and Silversmiths' Work' was sold at Christies.[12] A note in the sale catalogue states that these objects had been 'Removed from a Private Museum in the country which was built by an ancestor of the Present Owner about the year 1800'. There is no evidence from what we know of the Clarke family, however, to suggest that serious antiquarianism ever played a part in the formation of this 'collection'.

But it is perhaps worth considering the class of antiquary/collector which survived into the twentieth century. The generosity of four such, Alfred Maskell (d.1912), Fred Roe (d.1947), Aymer Vallance (d. about 1943) and Francis Eeles (d.1954) enriched the V & A collection. Alfred Maskell was for many years associated with the South Kensington Museum. He was unofficially attached to the Art Library from 1874 to 1876. He visited major international European exhibitions in an official capacity and, in 1880, was appointed to represent the South Kensington Museum in the acquisition of Russian art. For many years he was in charge of the private museum owned by Lord Brassey in Park Lane.[13] Fred Roe single-handedly promoted the subject of English oak furniture at a time when there was virtually no literature on the subject. His books were illustrated by the author's own pencil drawings which he had made on site. In fact, throughout his life Roe was a very productive professional portrait, historical and genre painter. Like Maskell, Vallance and Eeles he formed a small collection of medieval woodwork fragments. Aymer Vallance's two books on English church screens are models of their kind. They predicate a familiarity with a vast range of material, a characteristic shared by Francis Eeles. Both men were scholarly archaeologists. But Eeles was something more, an administrator with a gift for pleading the cause of English artistic culture. As Secretary for the Central Council for Care of Churches, for nearly forty years, he motored all over England to advise on the maintenance and restoration of churches and cathedrals.

Up to 1939 the museum displayed the whole of its collection of English medieval woodwork and furniture (FIG.1). As the building has grown the display locations have changed. In the early days the material was accommodated in a corridor gallery on the north-west side of the central courtyard. At the beginning of the twentieth century the new Aston Webb block, opened in 1909, allowed wholesale reorganisation. On the lower ground floor to the west of the entrance hall, where the Jones Collection now is, the first room comprised the museum's collection of European medieval woodwork and furniture. Some time later the space above and to the north, now occupied by the shop, was devoted to architectural woodwork including the massive sixteenth-century house-front from Sir Paul Pindar's house in Bishopsgate, London, which is still in the same position.

Since the return of the museum exhibits from storage at the end of the Second World War English medieval woodwork and furniture has held only a marginal and precarious share of the museum's display space. The bulk of the collection was not reinstated at South Kensington and remains to this day in store at Osterley Park. Up to about 1966 a few items were shown at the west end of Room 74, and in about 1980 a small display was created in Room 48 but this in 1987 disappeared to make way for an expansion of the shop. A few items are shown in the new medieval art and design galleries on the south and east sides of the courtyard, and a larger selection will be shown in the projected furniture materials and techniques gallery. The intention is that the bulk of the material will be housed in the near future at Blythe Road, Hammersmith, and will be accessible as a research collection. The museum's medieval woodwork is the victim of circumstance. It once occupied a prominent position. If it had been shown in a less conspicuous gallery it

FIG 1 V & A Museum. St. Nicholas, King's Lynn, Woodwork collection (part).

might still be enjoying a modest but secure slot in the hierarchy. In the event like many of its components, it has been conferred a refugee status.

The museum's fluctuating record in the display of its English medieval woodwork is a reliable barometer of scholarly and public esteem over the last one hundred or so years. It must be said that there was a time when a careful study of the subject was considered central to a good architectural education. The Victorians treated medieval woodwork as a branch of architecture. As such it comprised an important department of the treasury of decorative motifs and ornament offered by English medieval art. An ambitious architecture student in the nineteenth century considered a familiarity with the minutiae of medieval architecture and decorative sculpture to be a *sine qua non* of his professional competence. His knowledge of the subject came from sketching and drawing monuments in the flesh. He would have disdained the methods of the modern art-historian whose view of a monument is so often restricted to that obtained through the lens of a camera. The equivalent of photography in the early nineteenth century were the engravings produced by skilful professionals such as the antiquary John Britton's John Le Keux. These craftsmen provided more or less accurate views of monuments to illustrate an architect or antiquary's thesis. Such was the general level of interest in medieval ornament amongst an antiquarian-minded public that it profited publishers to produce books of designs. They aptly encapsulate the very different preoccupations of our ancestors. One of the finest is J.D. Harding's book of *Pugin's Gothic Ornaments*, published in 1831. J.K. Colling's titles – *Gothic Ornaments* (1845-50), *Details of Gothic Architecture* (1852-56), *Art Foliage* (1852-56) and *Medieval Foliage* (1874), are redolent of a reverence for the products of the medieval master-mason and master-carver's chisel. This kind of book was still in demand in the early twentieth century. For example, Ralph and J. Arthur Brandon's, *An Analysis of Gothic Architecture*, originally published in 1847, was reissued in 1903. In addition many architects' measured drawings of important English monuments were published at the end of the nineteenth century in sumptuous periodical folio editions such as the *Architectural Association Sketch Book*, *The Spring Gardens Sketch Book* and *John O'Gaunt's Sketch Book*.

Professional architects were not, of course, the only people who recorded monuments. There was a vigorous class of antiquary, often clergy or the sons thereof, who brought to the subject, apart from drawing skills, a classical education and often a profound knowledge of English ecclesiastical, liturgical and political history. John Parker's drawings of Welsh screens, some illustrated by Crossley and Ridgway, are a priceless record of church woodwork in the mid nineteenth century. Parker (1798-1860) was educated at Eton and Oriel College, Oxford, matriculating in 1816, and graduating B.A. in 1820 and M.A. in 1825. From 1827-1844 he was rector of Llanmarewic in Montgomeryshire at which period he was an increasingly active amateur architect. In 1835 he built the chancel and vaulted apse of Trinity Church, Oswestry. In 1844 he moved to Llan-y-Bladwell, Shropshire, where at his own cost he rebuilt the church to his own designs, even carving the altarpiece himself.[14]

Due to the paucity of English examples nineteenth-century studies of medieval domestic furniture were orientated towards France and the Netherlands. Even Henry Shaw's book, *Ancient Furniture*, among the few serious studies of English domestic furniture published last century, included several foreign examples. An interest in Continental domestic furniture was fed by the importation of specimens to complement the antiquarian country-house interiors created by decorators and dealers like John Webb. Otherwise an interest in the subject had to be satisfied by Viollet-le-Duc's, thoroughgoing *Dictionnaire Raisonné du Mobilier Français* (1858) and, later, Henry Havard's *Dictionnaire de l'ameublement de la décoration, depuis le XIIIe siècle jusqu'à nos jours* (1887-90). Both books include reconstructions of room interiors, some based on manuscript illuminations, others largely imaginary.

It was not until 1904 that a serious study of 'The Age of Oak' in English domestic furniture, to use Macquoid's designation, was published. This nomenclature was convenient because oak was regarded as the normal material for furniture in England, and elsewhere, up to the Restoration, and the surviving medieval output, such as it was, could thus be embraced in a work covering the 'medieval tradition' yet at the same time based upon a satisfactory number of specimens. Macquoid's three-part history of English furniture was rightly described by Ralph Edwards as 'pioneering'. His volume on oak furniture was one of the principal bases for *The Dictionary of English Furniture* (First edition 1924-27), for which Edwards was mainly responsible, although Macquoid was credited as part-author.

The published output of the redoubtable Fred Roe started in 1902 with his innovating *Ancient Coffers and Cupboards*. This was followed in 1905 by *Old Oak Furniture*. Roe frequently contributed articles to *The Connoisseur* and never missed an opportunity to champion the cause of 'Early English' woodwork and furniture. The only other important book on the subject to appear early in the century was Cescinsky and Gribble's, *Early English Furniture and Woodwork* (1922). The approach to matters of style and technique in these works can be characterised as typological and chronological. It was not until well after the Second World War that a serious attempt has been made to set medieval domestic furniture in its social context. Works such as Margaret Wood's *The English Medieval House* (1965) and Mark Girouard's *Life in the English Country House* (1978) point up the vastly different approach to scholarship which has opened up in the intervening years.

At the beginning of the twentieth century the output of scholarship on medieval domestic furniture was a trickle by comparison with the relative torrent of words expended on the subject of ecclesiastical woodwork. In first place should be mentioned the works of Francis Bond, on screens and galleries, fonts and font covers, choir-stalls and misericords. For their time these books are in a class of their own, and, by any standards, models of thoroughness and reliability. Their primary contribution was to catalogue and date the surviving material. Other books on the subject from this early stage of twentieth-century scholarship are Alfred Maskell's, *Wood Sculpture* (1911); F. Bligh Bond and B. Camm's, *English Church Screens and Roodlofts* (1909); J.C. Cox's, *Church Furniture* (1907), *Bench ends in English Churches* (1916), and *Pulpits, Lecterns and Organs in English Churches* (1915); and J.C. Cox and A. Harvey's, *English Church Furniture* (1907).

Only four scholars – Crossley, Ridgway, Howard and Vallance – studied English church wood-work in any depth. Fred Crossley (1899-1983), an architect from the north-east who spent his career in general practice designing schools, picture palaces, department stores and railway stations,[15] wrote papers on stallwork in Lancashire and Cheshire. In addition, over a period of some thirty years he and Maudie Ridgway recorded the surviving medieval ecclesiastical woodwork through-out Wales. Their findings were published in *Archaeologia Cambrensis* between 1943 and 1962. There were no doubt professional and logistical reasons why Crossley never extended his study of English church woodwork beyond the confines of Wales and his home area.[16] He knew the major monuments, of course, and photographed omnivorously. His *English Church Craftsmanship* (1941) is a distillation of a lifetime's knowledge and reflection but does not qualify as in-depth research. With no denigration to his scholarship it is arguable that Crossley's greatest contribution to the subject was his unique collection of over 10,000 high quality photographic negatives. Thanks to his generosity these are available for use by scholars today.

The research of possibly the century's most dedicated student of the subject, Frank Howard, was enshrined in Howard and Crossley's *English Church Woodwork* (1917), a model of high quality letterpress book production. Howard's text and measured drawings evince a real love of and flair for the subject. He was a successful practising ecclesiastical architect with little time for antiquarian publishing.[17] Almost certainly, had he not died young, his contribution to the subject would have been considerably greater.

A special word needs to be said about the study of misericords. Ever since the pioneering works of Thomas Wright in the mid-nineteenth century this has tended to be a rather specialised field. As with his work on choir-stalls Francis Bond's book on misericords is a classic. In its treatment of the iconographical problems raised by the subjects on the carvings it is good enough to stand comparison with Émile Mâle. Since then, important articles have been contributed by George Druce and books by Mary Anderson. In 1969 a complete catalogue of misericords in Great Britain was made available for the first time (Remnant 1969). More recently Christa Grössinger has published an extract from her doctoral thesis on English misericords and their relationship to manuscript illumination. Her article includes some convincing speculation about the origins of the device.

The main thrust of recent scholarship on English ecclesiastical woodwork has been the invalu-able work of archivists and historians. For instance, J.S. Purvis's articles of 1929 and 1935 on the 'Ripon School' of woodcarvers in the early sixteenth century, to use his coinage, is a pioneering study of English fifteenth- and sixteenth-century ecclesiastical furniture making. Moreover, it is perhaps difficult for us to acknowledge that very few archaeological details of any importance seem to have escaped his eye. The great chronological procession of choir-stalls at Ripon, Manches-ter and Beverley have been unjustly neglected. Purvis's pioneering research on these and related monuments threw down the gauntlet to the modern art historian. This scholar showed us the value of using documentary sources as corroboration for stylistic analysis. In the fabric accounts at Ripon the name of the head of the workshop that made the choir-stalls, William Bromflet, *alias* William Carver, is given although, unfortunately, only mentioned elsewhere at Bridlington Priory. By the early sixteenth century the system of regional centres of production was well established. That Ripon was a major source of inspiration for north-country ecclesiastical furniture making at the end of the fifteenth and the beginning of the sixteenth centuries is certainly plausible.

The meticulous transcription of mainly royal accounts forms the basis of a very much more ambitious innovatory work by John Harvey. His *English Mediaeval Architects*, first published in 1954, has placed a wealth of personal and factual information about the life and times of English master-craftsmen from the thirteenth to the sixteenth centuries at the disposal of the interested art historian. Harvey has also written a valuable book on medieval craftsmen. The other important work of archival research is of course H.M. Colvin's contribution to A *History of the King's Works* (Vol.I 1963). This provides a note of all the references of woodworking in the royal accounts for the medieval period. William St John Hope's definitive volumes on the architectural history of Windsor Castle (1913) had already provided a transcription of the accounts relating to the making of the choir-stalls in the fourteenth- and fifteenth-century St George's Chapels. But Colvin's volume alerted scholars to the full spectrum of craftsmanship undertaken for the court. Without these exemplary contributions to historical scholarship my own work on English choir-stalls would have been very much less effective.

An area that is touched on very little in this catalogue is that of structural woodwork. This has always been a somewhat neglected field although, of course, the restoring Victorian architects had a working knowledge of the principles involved. Howard and Crossley and Cescinsky and Gribble amongst others illustrated the typology of church roof structures. Vernacular domestic and farm buildings also languished as a subject for serious study. However, since the birth of medieval archaeology as a respectable academic discipline, encouraged by the wholesale redevelopment of our cities, there has been a flowering of interest. The books of Cecil Hewett, with their remarkable drawn illustrations, have led the way for a reappraisal of this aspect of our medieval heritage. Hewett's dating techniques using the criterion of jointing have opened up new possibilities of problem solving where documentation is totally lacking.

A valuable piece of recent research on medieval furniture, both secular and ecclesiastical, English and Continental, has been conducted by Penelope Eames. In her *Furniture in England, France and the Netherlands from the Twelfth to the Fifteenth Centuries* (1977) she demonstrates the value of using written documentary sources such as wills and inventories in the interpretation of domestic medieval furniture. Her work is the only important specialist contribution to the subject made in recent years. She has extended our contextual awareness of furniture beyond the invaluable confines of the painted panels of the Flemish 'Primitives'. She discusses the function and status of different classes of domestic furniture in the Middle Ages on the basis of inventorial references. She also examines a representative selection of English pieces in terms of contemporary French and Netherlandish output. This an eminently sensible approach since throughout the history of English furniture the association between the crafts in all three territories has been intimate.

*   *   *

Inevitably the Victoria and Albert Museum's collection is biased towards finely carved fragments, refugees from lost ensembles of fitted furniture. For instance, bosses and corbels constitute representative fragments from roofs, the most massive and least collectable category of medieval carpentry. Standards, canopy fragments and misericords stand for lost stallwork. There is a very rare rood screen front complete with superstructure but, for the most part, detached panels and tracery heads recall lost rood and parclose screens. In the domestic arena assorted exterior corner posts, window frames, doors and doorways, and ceiling beams evoke the timber-framed houses so very much more common in the Middle Ages than those built in stone. Such buildings are, for the most part, preserved for us solely through the painfully nostalgic late eighteenth- and early nineteenth-century drawings of the Bucklers, John Carter, William Essex and other antiquarian artists. The collection includes some of the more spectacular individual panels taken from the late medieval interior wall cladding of demolished houses.

Understandably, complete specimens of medieval domestic furniture are few. There is a representative selection of chests, the most numerous category of medieval domestic furniture to survive. Apart from the chest front incorporating scenes from the life of the Virgin none is of outstanding quality. Tables, chairs, forms and stools are very sparsely represented. With the demotion of the so-called 'Prince Arthur's Cupboard', probably a piece of seventeenth-century Gothic survival, the 'Rufford' chest-front, a fine fifteenth-century carved panel from Flanders, the arcaded chests, undoubtedly of German origin, and virtually the entire category of 'beds' from the previous catalogue, the range of domestic furniture on offer is emasculated. On the other hand the fragment of a domestic hall screen from Brightleigh, Devon, a relatively new acquisition, and the writing desk *cum* book cupboard, whose dating has been moved back to the late fourteenth century, are remarkable and interesting survivals.

The strength of the collection undoubtedly lies in the fragments of ecclesiastical woodwork. Of first importance are the magnificent bosses from Bishop Grandisson's early fourteenth-century extension to the bishop's palace at Exeter. Of great interest also are the bosses almost certainly from the somewhat earlier oak rib vaults in the Lady Chapel at St Alban's Abbey. The boss bearing the image of a bishop is another very important acquisition since the catalogue was last published. It must have come from one of the earliest examples of our native speciality – the timber vaulted roof. Choir-stalls are, of course, one of the glories of English medieval joinery. The museum is lucky to have fragments from some of the most important sets of stallwork – a boss from Winchester Cathedral (not previously recognised as such nor included in the previous catalogue); the fragment of arcading from the chapel of the royal foundation of St Katherine's Hospital-by-the-Tower; fragments of choir-stalls from the fine collegiate church of St Nicholas, King's Lynn; and misericords from Wells and Lincoln Cathedrals, the Benedictine abbey at Malmesbury and St Nicholas, King's Lynn.

This catalogue succeeds and replaces the *Catalogue of English Furniture & Woodwork*, I, *Gothic and Early Tudor*, published in 1923, a second enlarged edition of which appeared in 1929. This earlier catalogue covered a slightly larger field than the present work, including as it did a number of early Renaissance items. Although brief *Gothic and Early Tudor* was a competent and professional work. Its author, Harold Clifford Smith, F.S.A. (1876-1960), was a versatile antiquary who published extensively on furniture, silver and jewellery. He served in the Department of Woodwork, as it then was, at the Victoria and Albert Museum from 1910 to 1936, retiring as Keeper. Smith was a close friend of the late Queen Mary (1867-1953); hence his best known work, the standard account of *Buckingham Palace* (1931).

I have attempted to put flesh on the bones of his catalogue which, for the most part, provided little in the way of analysis or commentary. For the sake of continuity the painted panels in the museum's possession, discussed in the previous catalogue, are retained here. Matters of technique are dealt with as they crop up. I have not had the opportunity to investigate the undoubtedly primitive origins of the use of true panel-and-frame construction. To my certain knowledge it goes back in the manufacture of choir-stalls as far as the middle of the thirteenth century.[18] Nor have the origins of so-called 'linenfold' and 'parchemin' ornament been methodically studied. Inevitably there is still a large number of objects which seem to merit little more than a brief entry. Some of these, however, may have secrets to divulge which I have failed to extract. Both the objects about which I have plenty to say and those which leave me silent are listed, described and, as far as possible, illustrated. This will allow readers to form their own opinions. With over three hundred objects a few mistakes and errors of judgement are inevitable. But at least this important collection of English medieval furniture and woodwork will be made available to a wider audience. It is to be hoped that such proselytism may help to return the subject to its former position in both public and official favour.

Notes

1. Tracy (1986a).

2. The choir screens were badly damaged during the air-raid of May 1942, but both were subsequently pieced together and reinstated by Mr Herbert Read, the distinguished ecclesiastical wood carver.

3. Acquired from the cathedral in the mid-nineteenth century.

4. Both carried out under the direction of George Gilbert Scott.

5. See *Descriptive Memoir* and *Catalogue of the Museum of Mediaeval Art collected by the late* L.N. Cottingham, London, 1850.

6. The wanton destruction of this house in the 1950's complete with timber ceiling from Crosby Hall says much about early post-World War II attitudes to conservation.

7. See John Physick, *The Victoria and Albert Museum*, Oxford, 1982, 33-45.

8. Smith (1923), CAT.303, 54, and Macquoid & Edwards (1924), II, 202, FIG.1.

9. George Gilbert Scott, A *Guide to the Royal Archiectural Museum*, *n.d.*, 2.

10. The woodwork item from the Peyre collection is the late 13th/early 14th century door, acq. no. 754-1895 (CAT.254).

11. See W.P. Authers (ed.), *Diary of a Devonshire Squire-1844. The Journal of John Were Clarke, Esquire of Bridwell, Uffculme*, Tiverton, 1982.

12. Two West-Country bench ends, CAT.201-202, were purchased at this sale.

13. See *Who Was Who*, 1897-1916. See CAT.87.

14. D.N.B., XLIII, 1895, 250.

15. See his biographical papers in the R.I.B.A. library.

16. From 1926 to 1939 he was a partner in the firm of Gray Evans & Crossley of Liverpool. In 1945 he was appointed County Architect for Derbyshire.

17. His MS. of a book on Local Variations of Style in English Parish Churches was published after his death. See F.E. Howard, *The Mediaeval Styles of the English Parish Church*, London, 1936.

18. Tracy (1987), 65-66.

ECCLESIASTICAL

PLATE 1 a-d Bosses from Berrynarbor Church, Devon (cat. 1)

ECCLESIASTICAL

All the objects, unless otherwise stated, are of oak.

DETAILS OF ROOFS

1-4
BOSSES, four, from a roof, rectangular, the sides with trefoiled openings for roof beams or ribs (PLS 1a-d).
1. The surface is covered with interlacing 'stiff-leaf' foliage. 2. From each corner springs a trefoil of foliage with fruit, possibly blackberries. 3. In the centre is a rosette with cruciform opening, surrounded by a circular band carved with nail-heads; in each corner is a 'stiff-leaf' trefoil. Background decorated with punched stars.
4. 'Ball-flower' motif in centre with 'stiff-leaf' trefoil in each corner. Background decorated with punched stars.
From Berrynarbor Church, Devon
Circ.1222-1926 given by Mr J.W.Schofield
Mid 13th century
15 x 28 x 27.5 cm
126 to 128-1908 and *Circ.1222-1926*
The church of Berrynarbor, between Lynton and Ilfracombe, was restored in 1887. The 'stiff-leaf' palmettes on these bosses are somewhat rigidly drawn and the treatment presents little variety. The mid-

ribs do not dive into the terminations of the leaves as, for instance, on the misericords at Exeter Cathedral or on the West-Front at Wells Cathedral ('Resurrection' tier). The mid-ribs are not button-shaped, either, as at Exeter and Wells, but elongated. Berries with framing leaves and the palmette device can be seen in stone at Wells Cathedral (FIG.2) and Glastonbury Abbey. The somewhat un-imaginative and restrictive handling of the foliage suggests the sculpture to be the work of a country craftsman. The juxtaposition of conventional 'stiff-leaf' ornament with naturalistic motifs is reminiscent of the treatment of the Exeter Cathedral misericords of the mid 1240s (Tracy 1985). The use of punching to produce a decorated background to the carving is a particularly interesting and unusual feature.

5-9
BOSSES, five, from a roof, carved in high relief with conventional foliage; one (No. 123) has, in addition, the head of an ecclesiastic wearing a mitre, another (No. 119) a figure of a crouching lioness; another (No. 124) a fragment, the head of a woman wearing

FIG 2 Wells Cathedral. Upper spandrel in nave, north side, bay 7-5. East. Detail.

PLATE 2 a-c Bosses of lioness, cleric and female head from former bishop's palace, Exeter (cat. 5-9)

a wimple (PLS 2a, b & c, 3 & 4).
Given by H.M. Office of Works
1335-40
H. 49.5 cm, Diam. 49.5 cm
119 to 121 & 123-4 1865

These bosses are from one of the first floor chambers of the extension to the Bishop of Exeter's palace erected by Bishop Grandisson (1327-69). The new apartments were added to the extreme west end of the existing complex of buildings, substantially the work of Bishop Brewer (1224-44). The conjectural plan by H.M.R. Drury is reproduced in Chanter 1932 (facing p. 27). During his episcopate (1292-1307) Bishop Bytton had added some private rooms for his personal use to the west of Brewer's Great Hall with a lesser hall above. By the early fourteenth century the palace was fully up-to-date in terms of amenities. Bishop Grandisson must, however, have shared his predecessor's aversion to the communal life of the great hall. He annexed the last piece of ground remaining at the west end of

the complex to construct a self-contained hall for himself including an inner parlour with south-facing bay windows, and kitchens below on the ground floor, and two spacious chambers above. The addition had a frontage of over twelve metres, and a total depth of eighteen and one third metres. Unlike the rest of the palace it consisted of three storeys.

Grandisson's extension was demolished in the mid-nineteenth century. However, Charles Tucker, the cathedral's architect, recorded the fact that one of the first floor chambers had been furnished with a floor of decorative tiles and a fine oak roof of 'ornamental cross beams' (Tucker 1846). In particular, he mentions the bosses of this roof, one of which displayed the carving of a mitred bishop, wearing amice and chasuble. Another showed a female in a hood and both were surrounded by foliage. Two adjoining cross beams carried the arms of Grandisson and Montacute on separate shields. Tucker suggested that the bosses were portraits of

FIG 3 Exeter Cathedral. East bay of nave. Lioness boss.

PLATE 3 Foliage boss from Bishop's Palace, Exeter (cat. 6)

Bishop Grandisson and his mother, who was of the Montacute family. He mentioned a third boss in the form of a crouching hound (this is presumably the museum's lioness), and three other bosses of foliage only. He stated that there were traces of red, black and white paint, and gilding remaining on the sculpture. There can be no doubt that the V&A's carvings are the ones described by Tucker. They accord well enough with the descriptions and the dimensions given.

There is no documented date for the extension to the bishop's palace. This is not surprising since the fabric rolls for Grandisson's episcopate are far from complete (Erskine 1983, viii). Given the pattern of *lacunae* in the records it seems likely that the building work was undertaken between 1335-40. If so, the wooden roof would have been designed by the master-mason, Thomas of Witney, in collaboration with the master-carpenter. From an inspection of the cathedral wages lists (Erskine 1981, 175-211 and Erskine 1983, 293-310) it does not seem that any of the craftsmen involved in making Bishop Stapledon's choir furniture or structural woodwork was employed on the roof of his successor's new palace extension. William of Membiri, the master-carver, was paid off when the work on the throne was completed. Robert of Galmeton remained as the cathedral master-carpenter until 1321.

Nonetheless, the drawing of the heads on the bosses can be compared to that on the bishop's throne. The angels and the man and woman on the cusp-ends of the great ogee arches of the throne share much in common with the later work. The treatment of the heads with broad and flat foreheads, sharply-cut brows, prominent cheek-bones, flat and widely spread noses, cleanly modelled upper lip and thin wide-spread lips are common to both series. The putative Montacute portrait exhibits a particular way of drawing the edge of the upper eye-lid, by means of a prominent raised band, which is also found on the throne heads. The foliage on the palace bosses is akin to that on the throne. The leaves on the head bosses are of the most common type used on the earlier monument. The boss from the palace with a spiralling stem giving off budded shoots is also characteristic of much of the foliage on the throne. Finally, the tiny head of Stapledon on the tabernacle high up on the northern gable of the bishop's throne provides an instructive parallel to the image of Grandisson carved, presumably, some twenty years later.

Of about the same date as the throne are the stone lion roof bosses in the east bay of the nave

(FIG.3). Their carving style is very close to the treatment of the lioness from the bishop's palace. Again, however, the possibility of continuity of craftsmanship is ruled out by the fact that Richard Digon, who carved these stone bosses left Exeter to work at Wells Cathedral soon after 1313.

10-12
BOSSES, three, carved in openwork with conventional foliage.
Given by the Architectural Association
Probably 14th century
W.16, 17.2 x 28 cm, W.17, 16.5 x 22.8 cm,
W.18, 12.7 x 20.32 cm
W. 16 to W. 18-1916
Formerly in the Royal Architectural Museum, Westminster. See Architectural Museum 1877, 25, Nos 500-502.

13
BOSS, or section of a moulded beam, from a roof, carved with two masks chin to chin, one grotesque, the other bearded and wearing a cap, both surrounded by conventional foliage.
Said to have come from Exeter.
14th century
25.4 x 2 x 17.8 cm
W.172-1923
The most datable feature is, perhaps, the voluted 'trefoil' leaf foliage which first appears in wood on the Wells and Ely Cathedral choir-stalls in the 1330s. However, it was a motif that was repeatedly used until well into the fifteenth century.

14-15
BOSSES, two, from a roof, one carved with a winged ox (symbol of St Luke) holding a label in its mouth; the other with a winged lion (for St Mark) with a similar label (PLS 5 & 6).
Given by A. W. Leatham, Esq
Early 15th century
Each: dia. 30.5 cm
W.34 and W.35-1924
Purchased by the donor in Salisbury.

16
BOSS, from a roof, carved with conventional foliage.
Given by A. W. Leatham, Esq
Early 15th century
25.4 x 30.5 cm
W.36-1924

PLATE 4 Foliage boss from Bishop's Palace, Exeter (cat. 7)

PLATE 5 Boss with winged lion (cat. 14)

PLATE 6 Boss with winged ox (cat. 15)

PLATE 7 Boss from St Alban's Abbey with hawthorn foliage (cat. 18)

PLATE 8 Boss from St Alban's Abbey with 'stiff-leaf' foliage (cat. 20)

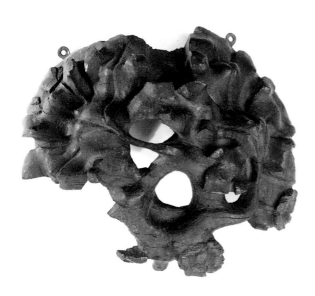

PLATE 9 Boss from St Alban's Abbey with maple foliage (cat. 22)

PLATE 10 Boss from St Alban's Abbey with oak foliage (cat. 23)

17-23

Bosses, seven, from a roof, circular, some having remains of gold and colour. One, No. 51, is carved with the head of a lion gnawing a bone (COL.PL.2); the remainder are carved in openwork with conventional foliage (PLS 7-10).

Early 14th century

No. 51, Diam. 50.8 cm, Nos.51c,d,e,f,i & j, Diam. about 35.6 cm

W.51,51c,51d,51e,51f,51i & 51j-1914

These bosses were removed from St Alban's Cathedral, Herts during the restoration of the Abbey about 1890. Thirteen in total were acquired by the museum, seven of which have been returned to the cathedral since the last edition of the catalogue. The large bosses, one with spiral pattern, the other with regularly arranged foliage stem and leaves, now on display at St Alban's, are from the choir vault. This must have been erected towards the end of the abbacy of Roger of Norton (1260-90).

The large boss displaying the lion gnawing a bone, and another now at St Alban's also showing a lion's head, must have been keystone bosses. All the others, smaller in size, must have been in secondary positions on the vault.

The museum's bosses are of early fourteenth-century type and are to be associated with the building activity of Abbot Hugh of Eversden (1308-26) who was responsible for the roofing of both Lady Chapel and retrochoir. Several types of foliage commonly used at this time are present, such as hawthorn, oak, maple and 'stiff-leaf' survival. In some the treatment is still naturalistic with two or more leaves springing from the same stalk (cf the boss in the museum from the Winchester Cathedral choir-stalls of 1308 et seqq., CAT.90, PL.35). Fruit and flowers are also present and the technique of juxtaposing leaves back and front is found. The leaves were gilded and their interstices painted red.

Some of the carvings are pierced right through over a large area and the profile of the whole boss is hemispherical. Interestingly, the underside of W.51J provides evidence for the surplus material having been removed on a turning lathe. At Winchester Cathedral the same regular grooving can be seen inside the finials of the choir-stalls reflecting the use of the same technique.

Most of the bosses probably come from the wooden vault of the Lady Chapel. Unfortunately, it has not been possible to recognise the large carving with the lion gnawing a bone from pre-restoration photographs of the ceiling. But it is difficult to imagine from where else this could have originated.

The flat ceiling in the retrochoir and the vaults of the Lady Chapel must have been made at much the same time. The bosses in the retrochoir must have all been about the same size and their style, as illustrated by Neale 1877, PL.52, is very like some of the museum's carvings. The presence of a boss from the choir vault in the original collection suggests that both Lady Chapel and retrochoir could quite possibly be represented.

A large number of bosses would have been required for the Lady Chapel and retrochoir ceilings. They could have been carved by a few master-carvers over a fairly wide time span (say, five years) or by a larger team over a shorter period. Some of the bosses are still quite naturalistically treated and, therefore, early in type. Others are reminiscent of the conventionalised Decorated style of carving of c.1315 as is exemplified at Chichester Cathedral on the vault of the Lady Chapel and the misericords of the choir-stalls. These differences may have been due to the presence of older and younger men employed in the same workshop.

24-27

Bosses, four, from a roof, rectangular.

1. In the form of a rose, with leaves at the angles. 2. A bunch of four openwork irregular serrated leaves springing from the centre, with similar leaves at the angles. 3. Overlapping serrated leaves springing from the centre. 4. Four openwork serrated leaves with pear-shaped bosses in the centre.

Given by W. Crewdson, Esq

Late 15th century

22.5 x 22.9 cm

118 to 121-1908

From Llanbadarn Fawr Church, near Aberystwyth, Dyfed. This type of non-structural boss is used in a purely decorative capacity in certain kinds of roofs from about 1400 onwards. It can be used to make a frieze on the wall plate or along each side of a tie-beam. Where the ceiling is divided into panelled compartments, at Ewelme, Oxon, for instance, groups of four bosses are sometimes applied to the panelling at the four corners of a rib intersection. An interesting three-dimensional composition can then be produced by placing a large boss at the point of intersection.

28

Boss, carved in openwork with maple foliage.

Given by the Architectural Association

Early 14th century

PLATE 11 a & b Scottish bosses with floral decoration and voluted 'trefoil leaf' (cat. 30-31)

17 x 30.5 cm

W.11-1917

Formerly in the Royal Architectural Museum, Westminster. The rounded profile of this boss, the rippling undulation of the foliage treatment, the robustness of handling and the cutting-away of the material beneath are all typical of the early Decorated style. The foliage is maple and there are traces of gilding and colour remaining on the surface.

29

Boss, square, carved with conventional foliage, the centre a shield of-arms – *three bends, the central bend between two engrailed cotices.*

15th century

22.8 cm square

W.25-1921

30-31

Bosses, two, from a roof. 1. Carved in the centre with a conventional flower resembling a lily; below it on either side extends a branch, on the top of which is perched a bird with a label in its beak. 2. Carved below with a rosette and above with interlacing scrolls terminating in trefoils (PLS.11a & b).

Scottish

15th century

(1) 38 x 3.5 cm (2) 28 x35.6 cm

W.107 and W.108-1926

So little Scottish medieval woodwork has survived that there is no stylistic context into which these bosses may be fitted.

32

Boss, from a roof, carved with conventional Gothic foliage.

From a Devonshire church.

Given by Mr A. L. Radford, F.S.A

Late 15th century

24.1 x 20.3 cm

W.196-1923

33

Boss, from a roof, carved with conventional Gothic foliage in two panels.

From a Devonshire church.

Given by Mr A. L. Radford, F.S.A

Late 15th century

21.6 x 21 cm

W.197-1923

34

Boss, from a roof, carved with the face of a devil.

From a Devonshire church.

Given by Mr A. L. Radford, F.S.A

Late 15th century

21.6 x 20.3 cm

W.198-1923

35

Boss, composed of cross motif with patera in centre.

15th century

13.6 x 12 cm

Circ.87-1921

36

Boss, composed of cross motif with patera in centre.

15th century

12.7 x 13.3 cm

Circ.88-1921

37

Boss, from the wooden rib vault of a church carved with the bearded head of a bishop, wearing a mitre, the background decorated with branches of pears and leaves (PL.12).

Probably English

About 1280

53.3 x 39.4 x 14.0 cm

W.10-1931

Although nothing is known about the provenance of this carving, we have to assume that it is probably English since so few church roofs on the Continent appear to have been constructed with wooden rib vaults. Quite possibly, like the other boss in the museum bearing the head of a bishop (CAT.8) it may have come from a domestic building with ecclesiastical associations.

Certain clues offer themselves as to dating, in particular the pear fruit and foliage, the tiny volutes on the extremities of the beard, and the way that the amice apparel stands away from the neck. The bust of the bishop is, of course, directly reminiscent of a tomb effigy. Little tight volutes on the beard can be found at Ely Cathedral on the effigy of Bishop Kilkenny, d.1256. The latter's amice apparel is worn in the same way as is that on the effigy of Bishop Bingham, d.1247, at Salisbury Cathedral (FIG.4). The prominent rubbery ears and eyelids of the V & A's boss are typical of English thirteenth century effigial sculpture. The hair protruding underneath the mitre (*cf.* Kilkenny at Ely or Brans-

PLATE 12 Boss with head of a bishop (cat. 37)

combe, d.1281, at Exeter) and the short beard and moustache (*cf.* Kilkenny and Bingham) are quite commonly found at this period.

The use of pear fruit is much harder to parallel in English medieval art of any period. If we look to the brief flowering of naturalism in England in the 1290s, we find very little soft fruit depicted at all, apart from the vine. A parallel can be cited from the spandrel sculpture in the chapter house at Southwell, *c.*1290 (B.O.E., *Nottinghamshire*, 324-25) where the intended fruit is more like an apple than

a pear. More convincing pear fruit and leaves can be found on the Cantilupe shrine (*c.* 1287) at Hereford Cathedral (B.O.E., *Herefordshire*, 167) (FIG.5).

38-40
CORBELS, three, from the base of wall posts of a roof, each in the form of a half-figure of an angel with curly hair holding a musical instrument, and supporting a battlemented projection. 1. The angel holds a harp, and wears a cape with ring-shaped collar, the lower garment and the sleeves carved

FIG 4 Salisbury Cathedral. Effigy of Bishop Bingham, d.1247. Detail.

FIG 5 Hereford Cathedral. Bishop Cantelupe's shrine. Spandrel.

PLATE 13 a, b & c Corbel of angels holding a harp, lute, and
lute or gittern (cat. 38-40)

FIG 6 St Wendreda, March, Cambs. Angel from base of hammer beam roof.

survived mainly intact. The positioning of a large tenon directly above the figures is rather puzzling since angel-figures on medieval church roofs were nearly always cantilevered out from the wall. On hammer-beam roofs it was common practice to incorporate, on the wall posts, an inhabited canopied niche below the springing of the brace. An angel with outstretched wings would be positioned below this or at an angle of thirty degrees to the wall. Also on hammer-beam roofs the angels could be placed at the same angle on the innermost extensions of the beams. They are also found fixed to the collars of the roof but, again, at an angle to the perpendicular. The arrangement in the V & A's specimens allows for the figures to project at an angle to the wall but restricts their function to that of 'corbels'.

The museum's angels, without or with only perfunctory wings, are too small to have been used on the roof of a major space. The use of angel figures in lesser contexts is not particularly common but an instance can be cited at Long Melford, Suffolk, in the south aisle of the Lady Chapel. The corbels here are used in association with a cambered tie-beam roof of modest span. The building of the Lady Chapel can be dated precisely to 1496 (B.O.E., *Suffolk*, 345). Stylistically, however, the museum's angels seem to be closest to those on the hammer-beam roof at March, Cambs of *c*.1500 (B.O.E., *Cambridgeshire*, 437) (FIG.6).

with feather-like ornament. 2. The angel holds a lute, and wears an alb with apparelled amice.
3. The angel holds a lute or gittern, and wears a cape covering the shoulders above a surplice (PLS 13a, b & c).
From a Suffolk church
Last quarter of 15th century
Each 61 x 21.6 x 22.9 cm
W.21 to W.23-1911
These corbels are said to have come from St Mary, Bury St Edmund's although it is difficult to imagine from where. They do, perhaps, remind us somewhat of the stone corbel-busts in the south aisle, which are similarly topped by a crenellated parapet. But there is nowhere for them on the magnificent timber roof of the nave which appears to have

41
CORBEL, in the form of a half figure of an angel holding a crown, and supporting a moulded projection.
From a Suffolk church
15th century
53.4 x 25.6 x 10.4 cm
W.24-1911
This figure is similar to the previous group of three in size and function. It does not seem to have come from the same church, however, as the moulded parapet is different in form and the author of the carving is clearly not the same.

42
CORBEL in the form of an angel. The figure, half-length, in alb and apparelled amice emerges from conventional clouds, the hair feathery, the hands raised in adoration (PL.14).
Second half of 15th century
63.5 x 30.4 x 17.8 cm
A.1-1910

PLATE 14 Angel corbel from Louth church (cat. 42)

FIG 7 St James, Louth, Lincolnshire. Angel figure from
dismantled 15th century nave roof.

This figure is said to have come from Louth Church, Lincolnshire, rebuilt in the fifteenth century. It was restored in 1869. There are two figures of angels from the original roof still in the church (FIG.7). The high quality of all three suggests that the original timber ceiling must have been very fine.

43

CORBEL. In front is the head of a bearded king, from whose ears spring Gothic leafage covering the sides of the corbel; above and below are the moulded terminations of an arch.
From the roof of the chapel of Farleigh Castle, Somerset
15th century
36.8 x 21 x 30.2 cm
1152-1904
This carving was purchased in 1904 at Farleigh Hungerford, where it had been preserved for many years. The chapel was rebuilt by Walter, Lord Hungerford, in the reign of Henry VI; it was repaired in 1779 and again in 1806.

44

CORBEL. The design is in the form of a mask with foliage springing from the corners of the mouth.
West Country.
Given by Mr T. Charbonnier
14th century
29.4 x 28 cm
246-1908

45

CORBEL, with flat three-sided top, supported by a crouching figure of an angel holding a shield (PL.15).
Second quarter 15th century
25.4 x 30.4 x 26.7 cm
W.26-1921
This corbel was formerly in the Royal Architectural Museum, Westminster. The drapery style is similar to that on the misericord in the museum from Malmesbury Abbey (CAT.87), probably of the middle of the fifteenth century A good comparison in alabaster is on the tomb of Sir John Cressy, d.1444, at Dodford, Northants (Arthur Gardner 1940, PL.27). The kneeling angels there exhibit the same plain single-ribbed upper wings and the thick plastic, almost tubular drapery. The arrangements of the hair in rolls is commonly found in the mid fifteenth century and can be seen, for instance, on the figure of Gabriel in the reredos of the Henry V chantry at Westminster Abbey of the 1440s (FIG.8). The heavy voluminous drapery with angular jagged folds was

FIG 8 Westminster Abbey. Figure of Gabriel from Annunciation group in Henry V chantry.

introduced to the Netherlands about 1430 from Italy. This is also to be seen on the Henry V chantry.

46-47

CORBELS, two, probably representing angels carrying shields.
Late 15th century
16.5 x 8.9 cm
W.5 & 6-1930
Said to have come from Melbourne, Derbyshire. These small figures probably decorated a church roof on wall plate or tie-beam.

PLATE 15 Corbel of angel holding a shield (cat. 45)

PLATE 16 Figure pilaster (cat. 48)

FIG 9 Metropolitan Museum of Art, New York (The Cloisters Coll.). Alabaster figure of St Fiacre.

48
PILASTER, possibly a wall-bracket from the roof of a church, in the form of a standing figure of a bearded man, probably a saint, holding a book in one hand (the other hand is missing). Above the head is a moulded capital (PL.16).
Given by Mr Frank Surgey, through the National Art-Collections Fund
Late 15th century
96.5 x 20.3 cm
W.7-1928
This figure must be from a roof where the wall posts were long enough to accommodate a small figure, presumably, standing on a corbel. The head-type, drapery and subject of the carving can be paralleled in fifteenth-century alabaster sculpture such as the St Fiacre figure in the Cloisters at the New York Metropolitan Museum (FIG.9) or another representation of the saint on an alabaster panel in the V&A (V&A Acq.No. A.135-1946. See Cheetham 1984, 102).

49
PAIR OF SPANDRELS, from a roof, carved in openwork with a series of circles decreasing in size and containing respectively four quatrefoils, a floral device, a single quatrefoil and a trefoil.
Early 15th century
W. 57, 55.8 x 129 cm, W. 57A, 53.4 x 124 cm
W.57 & 57A-1925
Said to have come from Wymondham Church, Norfolk.

50
BOSS FRAGMENT, probably from the intersection of roof ribs, with one central and two side branches carved with conventional foliage.
From a church in Aberdeen.
Given by Mr F. C. Eeles, in memory of the late Professor Cooper, Professor of Church History in Glasgow University, founder in 1886 of the Aberdeen Ecclesiological Society (afterwards the Scottish Ecclesiological Society)
Late 15th, or early 16th century
61.2 x 26.7 cm
W.23-1923
Probably from the choir of St Nicholas, Aberdeen; or possibly King's College, Aberdeen, or the nave of Aberdeen Cathedral. It resembles the work of John Fendour who erected the ceiling in the parish church of St Nicholas between 1495 and 1515 (Kelly 1934, FIG.5). He probably made the ceiling of King's College Chapel also (Macpherson 1889, 11 & FIGS LVII, LX, LXI & LXIII and Eeles 1956).

51
PORTION of a ROOF BRACE, of bracket shape, carved
on both sides with a rose and leaves; the edge is
moulded, above are two large tenons.
From Deddington Church, Oxfordshire
About 1500
119 x 30.4 x 16.5 cm
W.145-1921

52
Boss, carved and painted, in the form of a half-
length angel holding a shield of arms.
15th century
43.8 x 24.7 x 12.9 cm
W.70-1929

53
Boss, of convex form. In the centre a grotesque
animal, possibly a greyhound, surrounded by
foliage.
15th century
13.5 x 43.8 x 24.7 cm
W.71-1929

54
Boss, carved with four leaves divided by tendrils
and quatrefoil petals. Mounted on an oak board.
15th century
7.8 x 20.3 x 24.7 cm
W.72-1929

55
Boss, carved with four leaves with interlacing stems.
Late 15th century
H. 1.8 cm, L of side. 20.3 cm
214-1897

56
Portion of a Boss.
Given by T. Charbonnier
15th or early 16th century
29.2 cm x 15.3 cm
252-1908

DOORS

57-58
Two Doors, each being half of a pair of folding doors, from arched doorways. Each door, which is of slightly different design, is divided by ribs into four panels; on the lower part is a band of cusped arches (missing on one door); the upper part where the ribs intersect is filled with varieties of geometrical tracery. Each door has two iron strap hinges with ring sockets (PLS. 17a & b).

From St Mary, Beverley, Yorkshire

W.5, Second decade 15th century; W.5a, Mid 15th century

W.5 about 30 x 104 cm; W.5a 31 x 104 cm

W.5 and W.5a-1921.

Acquired in 1921 from the Royal Architectural Museum, Westminster, having been sold at auction in 1851. The left-hand door (W.5) belonged to the entrance doorway of the south porch, the building

PLATE 17 a & b Two doors from St Mary, Beverley (cat. 57-58)

of which dates from the second quarter of the 15th century (See Bilson 1926, 401). The right-hand door (W.5a) is the eastern leaf from the south transept doorway. This part of the church was built *c.*1450-60 (See Bilson 1920, 409-10). The other leaf of this door is still *in situ* and is the only medieval door that remains in the church. They were probably taken out and disposed of at the time of the restoration of these parts of the church under A.W.N. Pugin and his son, E.W. Pugin, between 1844 and 1859 (See Bilson 1920, 401 and Bilson 1926, 340). These doors display the refinement of tracery drawing typical of the region during the first half of the fifteenth century, *e.g.* Boston Church, west door (FIG.10). The delicacy of handling, exploits the special characteristics of the medium.

59-61
PANELS, three, possibly from the porch of a church, each pierced with two cusped openings and a quatrefoil above.
East Anglia
Given by Mr A.H. Fass
14th century
43.2 x 25.4 cm
W. 152 to W.152b-1921

FIG 10 St Botolph, Boston, Lincolnshire. West door.

62-65

PANELS, four, probably from a reredos, painted with four groups from a series representing the Nine Choirs of Angels, *viz.*, Principalities, Powers, Archangels and Thrones. Now framed as a pair of doors (COL.PL.3).

Principalities. Five winged figures in standing position, with four seated figures below. The angelic figures have large crown-like head-dresses and wear robes trimmed with fur, two of them adorned with conventional devices in gold. The figures in the foreground represent a bishop and a pope on the left, a king and queen on the right. The bishop wears cope and mitre, the pope a triple-crowned tiara. On a scroll above the central figure is a label with the words: "Salve radix iese"; on a scroll

FIG 11 King's College, Cambridge. Charter of 1446. Detail of the two Houses of Parliament.

below are the words: "Principatus presunt bonis hoibus."

Powers. Five figures winged, in armour and surcoats, trampling on and binding winged demons. One unsheathes a sword, the next two are pulling the rope, a fourth holds a scourge like a black broom, and the fifth is about to strike with a sword. Their armour is white; over it they wear dark-coloured surcoats. One holds a scroll. Beneath is the inscription:. "Potestates presunt demonibus."

Archangels. Five figures in albs, apparelled amices and dalmatics. The central figure holds a cruciform church with a spire; he is in a red dalmatic. On the left is another figure in a red dalmatic, on the right one in a dalmatic with horizontal bands of gold embroidery; these two hold a scroll. Of the other two figures, that on the left is in green and that on the right holds the model of another cruciform church with a central spire. All the angels have amice apparels; three have large apparels on their albs. Beneath the scene are the towers of a city. On a scroll below are the words: "Archangeli presunt civitatibus."

Thrones. Three winged figures seated in robes decorated with stars, with white capes and hoods, and in the attitude of giving judgment, each raising a hand; at their feet are two smaller figures bearing an inscribed scroll; below, the words: "[T]roni emunt judicare."

Mid 15th century (The framework probably early 17th century)

180 cm x 91 cm. Each panel, 68.5 x 43.2 cm

W.34 to W.34c 1912

The hierarchy of angels is supposed to stem from Jewish apocryphal literature but appears for the first time in a Greek treatise 'On the Celestial Hierarchy', supposed to have been written by Dionysius the Areopogite, but actually composed in the fifth or sixth century. There were nine orders of angels. The first group comprised Seraphim, Cherubim and Thrones; the second, Dominions, Virtues and Powers; and the third; Principalities, Archangels and Angels. In the first group Thrones typify perfect rest and contemplation as being nearest to God. In the second group Powers represent the office of resisting and casting out devils. In the third group Principalities are entrusted with the rule of nations, princes and cities. Archangels were God's special ambassadors (For the full iconography of the Nine Orders of Angels see Chatwin 1928, Rushforth 1936, and Woodforde 1950).

These panels are stated to have come from a Northamptonshire church. Nicholas Rogers has said that: 'the fluted armour worn by the Powers suggests a date near the middle of the fifteenth century'. He feels that this detail: 'is probably more significant than the bowl crop well clear of the ears most evident in the Archangels panel'. He draws a stylistic parallel with the early work of William Abell, such as the King's College, Cambridge Charter of 1446, 'which displays similar hard facial types with heavy eye-lids' (FIG.11). Rogers has tentatively suggested that 'the panels are the work of a London rather than an East Anglian atelier of the 1440s'.

It has not been possible to find precise parallels for the inscriptions. Rogers points out that: 'The stained glass at All Saints' Church, York includes similar captions assigning particular qualities to each of the orders, but the inscriptions do not correspond'.

MISERICORDS

66

MISERICORD; the projecting support is shaped and moulded, and has below it the figure of a crouching man, his feet curled up beneath him, his elbows raised to the level of his head (PL.18). The moulding round the edge is continued as volutes on each side, and terminates with a leaf carved in openwork relief. The seat is partly restored.

Said to have come from Wells Cathedral

About 1335-40

28.3 x 59 x 17.3 cm

W.48-1912.

This misericord agrees in style and design with the other misericords at Wells (see Church 1907, 319). The motif of a man 'shouldering' the bracket above him is one of the most commonly employed by sculptors on misericords. It has been shown to derive in some cases from the marginal illustrations, or drolleries, in illustrated manuscripts (Grössinger 1975). Such drawings can be found in the *Hours of Jeanne d'Evreux*, illustrated by Johan Pucelle, about 1300 to 1355, which was produced at about the same time as the Wells Cathedral choir-stalls. The choir

PLATE 18 Misericord from Wells Cathedral with crouching man (cat. 66)

Misericords   55

FIG 12 Wells Cathedral. 'Flight of Alexander' misericord.

furniture at Wells remained more or less intact until it was partly destroyed and partly rearranged by Anthony Salvin in 1848 to provide additional seating. On a combination of circumstantial and stylistic evidence a date of manufacture of 1335-40 is indicated (Tracy 1987, 25-29).

There were two master-carvers working on the choir-stalls, the so-called master of the 'Animals' and the master of the 'Flight of Alexander' (FIG.12). The latter was almost certainly the younger man and it must have been he who carved the museum's misericord. He worked in an advanced style using expressive poses. In the drapery of his human forms he demonstrates a considerable sophistication of technique. Grössinger has compared the style of his carving to that of Pucelle. However, the undoubted similarities in both poses and the handling of drapery do not necessarily identify this sculptor as a Frenchman.

67

MISERICORD; the projecting seat, which is six-sided with a slightly projecting point in front, is bordered with a sunk moulding carved at intervals with quatrefoil rosettes (PL.19). The carving below consists of foliage in high relief. The moulded edge

of the seat is continued as a stalk on either side and terminates in a carved leaf.
Said to have come from Lincoln Cathedral
About 1370
29.2 x 67.5 x 15.2 cm
W.104-1924

The date of the erection of the stalls at Lincoln is fixed within a fifteen-year period (1361-76) by the occurrence on the base of the dean's stall of the shields of Dean Stretchley and Bishop Buckingham. The date assigned to the furniture by Bond of about 1370 is quite acceptable (Bond Stalls, 53).

The voluted 'trefoil' leaf seen on the museum's misericord has a pedigree in the foliage repertory of fourteenth-century English decorative carving going back to the early years of the century. Prototypes of the motif can be seen on the St Alban's shrine (probably c.1302-08) and the bishop's throne at Exeter Cathedral (1312-17). Early examples of the canonical form in stone can be seen in the north porch of St Mary Redcliffe, Bristol (c.1320) and on a roof boss in the crypt of St Stephen's Chapel, Westminster (probably c.1320).

Of special interest is that an identical treatment of this sort of leaf occurs on the slightly earlier choir-stalls made for St Katherine's Hospital-by-the-

PLATE 19 Foliage misericord from Lincoln Cathedral (cat. 67)

Tower (CAT.89). It has been a matter of controversy as to whether the Lincoln choir-stalls, and, indeed, those at Chester Cathedral, which must have been made by the same workshop, were made by carpenters from London or the north of England. The close stylistic correspondences between the carving in both cathedrals and that at St Katherine's strongly suggests that the cathedral furniture was the work of metropolitan craftsmen. We are probably dealing with the workshop formed to make the final set of choir furniture for St Stephen's Chapel, Westminster (now destroyed), one of the most important ecclesiastical furniture commissions of the fourteenth century. If this is the case, we should acknowledge that the master-carver concerned, Master Edward of St Andrew, came, originally, from Nottinghamshire and most of his assistants from south Yorkshire (Tracy 1987, 49-55).

68
MISERICORD. The projecting support rests on the reclining nude figure of a bearded man leaning his head on his left hand. Part of the seat has been broken off and the front of the support is damaged (PL.20).
Said to have come from East Anglia

Mid 14th century
24.1 x 60.3 x 13 cm
W.25-1911
The conceit of a naked, probably sleeping, man lying stretched out on his side supporting the misericord on his back is aesthetically successful. The absence of any supporters dramatizes the formal idea. The figure has a certain rustic charm yet, in this case, if we compare it to the only other similar naked figure on a misericord at Darlington Parish Church, of the fifteenth century (FIG.13), it is evident that the model from which the artist worked must have been itself a work of some ambition. The figure has a certain expressive quality, and a tautness as of a coiled spring, that demands our attention. By comparison the Darlington figure is flabby and anatomically unconvincing. The use of supporters there only tends to clutter up the composition.

The misericord is said to have come from East Anglia and has been assigned to the fifteenth century. A glance at the Darlington figure tells us at once that the carvings cannot be of the same period. The treatment of the hair and the expressively large hands recall the figures on the portals of Romanesque churches, although the pose speaks to

PLATE 20 Misericord with crouching man (cat. 68)

us of Gothic art. Because this sculpture is only a faint echo of a distinguished metropolitan model it is not an easy object to date. The broad curving bracket of the seat is quite similar to those at Winchester or Chichester Cathedrals of the early fourteenth century. The head-type and large expressive hands with long fingers is reminiscent of the drawing in the early fourteenth century de Lisle Psalter (BL.MS.Arundel 83). I refer to the paintings in the first psalter (fls 1-116 verso), probably made for Sir William Howard of East Winch, near King's Lynn, Norfolk (d.1308), or for his wife Alice de Fitton (Rickert 1965, 241, n.44). The head-type is also not dissimilar to that found in the effigy of Edward II at Gloucester Cathedral of about 1330-35 and to a misericord, also at Gloucester, depicting a naked 'Green Man' (FIG.14). Again, the man is asleep, with his head resting on his hand. He too has long flowing hair and a beard. But there are important differences in the Gloucester figure compared to the V&A's carving. Although he is naked, he is supposed to be covered in thick hair which is indicated on the body by means of incised lines. Moreover, the figure is conventionally placed, vertically, in the centre of the misericord. Consequently, the upper torso only is visible. In the circumstances, it would

FIG 13 St Cuthbert, Darlington, Yorkshire. Reclining man misericord.

be wise to assign the museum's carving simply to the first half of the fourteenth century.

The outstanding problem is the identification of the figure on this very unusual misericord. The most likely candidate is Adam, but what is he doing in a reclining position? He is most often depicted with Eve standing next to the Tree of Knowledge, being expelled with her from the Garden of Eden, or being rescued from Hell by Christ in the 'Har-

FIG 15 Salisbury Cathedral. Detail from 'Creation of Eve' scene in chapter house arcade sculpture.

FIG 16 Hereford Cathedral. Reclining Old Testament personage misericord.

FIG 14 Gloucester Cathedral. 'Green Man' misericord.

rowing of Hell' episode. A prone figure of Adam on his own is much more unusual although it does occur sometimes at the foot of the Cross in Crucifixion scenes. In these cases he can be seen, usually clothed, but sometimes naked, rising from his tomb which was located on the same spot as Christ's crucifixion. The two different phases of the Creation of Adam were sometimes illustrated – his sculpting from clay and God breathing life into him. None of these images, however, seem appropriate in this case. However, if we turn to the event of the Creation of Eve, we find that Adam was asleep during the proceedings: 'And the Lord God caused a deep sleep to fall upon the man, and he slept; and he took one of his ribs, and closed up the flesh instead thereof: And the rib, which the Lord God had taken from the man, made he a woman, and brought her unto the man' (Genesis, 2,21). It would seem that the iconography of this scene would be much more likely to answer our case. Indeed, if we examine the event as shown in the arcade sculpture in the thirteenth-century Chapter House at Salisbury Cathedral, we find Adam reclining, naked and asleep, just as he is on the misericord (FIG.15). Better still, perhaps, is the figure of a naked man on a misericord at Hereford Cathedral of c.1345 (FIG.16). Incongruously he retains an important article of clothing, the peaked hat which was used at this time to distinguish characters from the Old Testament. Admittedly he is awake. Perhaps there was a carving of the newly created Eve on the adjacent misericord of the choir-stalls for which the museum's carving was made.

69-72
FOUR MISERICORDS; the seats, bordered with a six-sided double moulding with a tapering and facetted support to the bracket (PLS 21-24); below are carved three harvesting scenes – stooking (W.8), carting (W.53) and threshing the corn (W.7), and the image of an eagle with a scroll in its beak, flanked on either side by grotesque figures (W.52).
Probably from East Anglia
Late 14th century

PLATE 21 Threshing misericord (cat. 69)

PLATE 22 Stooking misericord (cat. 70)

PLATE 24 Carting the corn misericord (cat. 72)

PLATE 23 Eagle misericord (cat. 71)

FIG 17 Worcester Cathedral. Misericord with corn reaping.

W.7, W.8 & W.53, 29.2 x 57 x 15.3 cm,
W.52. 29.2 x 56 x 15.3 cm
W.7, W.8, W.52 and W.53-1921

These misericords were purchased, with the six below (CAT.73-78) from the Royal Architectural Museum, Westminster. It had been assumed that all ten misericords were from St Nicholas, King's Lynn until Remnant (1969, 94) pointed out the differences in design in the seats. These carvings must, indeed, come from a different, and unidentified, set of choir-stalls.

The harvesting scenes were probably associated with a cycle of the labours of the month and copied from calendar illustrations. Such cycles are likely to have been common but, unfortunately, all that is left is a few individual misericords. All three of the

subjects displayed on the museum's carvings are unique. Considering the popularity of these cycles in manuscript illumination, it is surprising that there are only six examples in England of the cutting of corn on misericords (FIG.17).

Of equal interest in this set of carvings is the treatment of the supporters. There are a pair of pygmies, two pairs of half-humans, half-animals and a pair of so-called blemyae. The latter are from the repertory of fantastic creatures mentioned by Pliny in *Natural History* and later in books such as *Mandeville's Travels* written in French about 1357. The blemya or anthropopaghus was a man with no head and a face in his chest. He is described in a fifteenth-century translation of *Mandeville's Travels*: 'And in another yle also ben folk that han non hedes, and here eyen and here mouth ben behynde in here schuldres' (Seymour 1967, 147). Those illustrated in the *Livre des Merveilles* (Bib.Nat.ancien fonds français 2816), a collection of accounts of the Orient which includes *Mandeville*, show how these men were usually presented. The pair on the misericord of the thresher seem to be a conflation of blemya and pygmy. The more conventional treatment can be seen on the late fifteenth-century examples at Norwich (FIG.18) and Ripon catherdrals.

These four misericords are quite distinct from the group of six seats from St Nicholas King's Lynn (see below) church. They could be from East Anglia but they are probably slightly earlier in date than the King's Lynn furniture, that is, of the late fourteenth century.

73-78

SIX MISERICORDS; the seats bordered with a four-sided double moulding; flanked by foliage and other decorative supporters (PLS 25-30). The subjects of the carvings consist of: A leopard gorged and chained, on the left a merchant's mark, and on the right a barrel and a hook, each in ribbon letters (W.6); An ecclesiastic, apparently the donor, kneeling at prayer; he is vested in a long full surplice, hood and round cap; on the left a twisted ribbon in the shape of the letter 'B,' enclosing an eagle displayed; on the right a 'Y,' with a pod, probably the donor's device (W.9). A falcon grasping a rabbit; on either side a pomegranate (W.10); A stag pursued by hounds; on the left a hunting horn, on the right a crossbow, each in ribbon letters (W.11); A lion crouching; on either side a rose. On the back are cut the words: 'W. H. Hubbard, March 19, 1775,' and the letters 'E P, 1769.' (W.12); and a master-carver seated at his bench, with his dog at his feet, designing with the aid of dividers and square, while two apprentices are busily carving on the left, and another brings a jug. In the background is a completed tracery-head, also two lengths of cresting, fret-cut but not carved, also a plank. On the left of the group is a twisted ribbon forming the letter 'W' enclosing a saw; on the right the letter 'V' and a gouge (W.54).
From St Nicholas, King's Lynn
About 1419
W.6., 24.3 x 63.5 x 15.3 cm, W.9., 25.4 x 56 x 12.7 cm, W.10., 25.4 x 63.5 x 12.7 cm, W.11., 25.4 x 54.6 x 12.7 cm, W.12., 25.4 x 635 x 14.0 cm, W.54., 25.4 x 56 x 15.3 cm
W. 6, W. 9, W. 10, W. 11, W. 12 and W. 54-1921
The Chapel of St Nicholas, King's Lynn was founded

FIG 18 Norwich Cathedral. Blemya misericord supporter.

by William Turbe, Bishop of Norwich, 1146-74, for the use of the inhabitants of the New Lande he had laid out for building north of the Purfleet. His chapel was pulled down and on its site was built a small chapel, the west end of which, probably dating from 1200-1210 (Beloe 1900, 95), remains. The present building was constructed in the early years of the fifteenth century and completed about 1419 (Beloe 1900, 111). These misericords and many other carvings from St Nicholas, evidently part of the original fitted wooden furnishings, were sold by the churchwardens in 1852 and bought by the Royal Architectural Museum (H. Smith 1923, 28-29 and Architectural Museum 1877, 53).

There can be no doubt whatsoever that this group of six misericords is from St Nicholas' Chapel. Some of the woodwork is still *in situ* and telling details, on both the loose carvings and the fitted furniture still in the church, are found in common. The museum also bought a number of bench-ends (CATS.158-83). In its original arrangement the woodwork must have been very impressive. It is a tragedy that the nineteenth-century ecclesiologists elected to tidy it up. The poppy-heads, now in the chancel of the church, are some of the finest in England. The misericords are also of high quality.

PLATE 25 Misericord from St Nicholas, King's Lynn, with
gorged and chained leopard (cat. 73)

PLATE 26 Misericord from St Nicholas, King's Lynn, with
ecclesiastic at prayer (cat. 74)

PLATE 27 Misericord from St Nicholas, King's Lynn, with
falcon and rabbit (cat. 75)

PLATE 28 Misericord from St Nicholas, King's Lynn, with
stag and hounds (cat. 76)

PLATE 29 Misericord from St Nicholas, King's Lynn, with
crouching lion (cat. 77)

PLATE 30 Misericord from St Nicholas, King's Lynn, with
master-carpenter (cat. 78)

The carving of the master-carpenter is well known. There are a few other misericords in England showing the carpenter at work (FIG.19) but the museum's composition is one of the most informative. Another misericord displays contemporary wooden furniture. The carving with the ecclesiastic kneeling at prayer, possibly the donor of the woodwork, shows a bench with high, crested back and a reading desk not unlike the one in the museum's collection (CAT.314, PL.114a,b & c).

Another carving shows a bird of prey in the act of catching a rabbit. This subject is often found on misericords. An example from Stowlangtoft in Suffolk of about the same date makes a good comparison (FIG.20). On the King's Lynn carving other rabbits are peeping out of their burrows. This motif also occurs in two elaborately carved chest fronts at the V & A, one from Rufford Old Hall, Lancs (Acq.No.82-1893) of mid fifteenth-century date and probably Flemish, and the other of unknown provenance, possibly from the late fourteenth century and probably English (W. 15 and 15a-1920, CAT.300, PL.106). Another carving from this group worthy of special mention is the misericord of the gorged and chained spotted leopard (CAT.73, PL.25). Perhaps the devices on the supporters here suggest that one of the donors of this very elaborate furniture was a ship's chandler, an appropriate occupation in a thriving medieval seaport.

79-86

EIGHT MISERICORDS with carving in the centre depicting foliage or figurative scenes and foliage supporters. The species depicted in the central carvings are vine (W.5, PL.32), rose (W.7) and pomegranate (W.10). Central figurative scenes depict Adam delving and Eve spinning (W.9), three cloaked heads before a trestle table (W.4, PL.31), feeding the swine (W.6), man with tongue out (W.8) and unidentified figure scene (W.11)
Early 16th century
26.7 x 48.3 x 11 cm
W.4 to W.11-1948

These misericords were removed from Blagdon church, Somerset about 1820. They are a mixture of figurative and purely decorative foliage carvings. The shape of the seats and the carving style compares very closely with the misericords at Worle Church a few miles away. The treatment of vine leaves and grapes in both sets, and the use of cloaked human heads (FIGS.21 & 22), strongly suggests that both sets of sculpture were by the same rustic carver. These misericords are examples of

FIG 19 All Hallows, Wellingborough, Northamptonshire. Misericord showing master-carpenter at work.

FIG 20 St George, Stowlangtoft, Suffolk. Falcon with rabbit misericord.

country craftsmanship at its best enlivened by naivety of inspiration and robustness of character. Since the subjects at Blagdon include feeding the swine, and Adam and Eve at their biblical occupations, it is quite possible that there was a Labours cycle here.

As it happens, the stalls at Worle can be dated precisely to the early years of the sixteenth century. One misericord there bears the letter P and the monogram R.S.P., the P probably standing for prior, and R.S. for Richard Spring, prior of Woodspring and vicar of Worle, 1499-1516 (Brassington 1925, 55). It is useful thus to be able to date the museum's carvings, despite the appearance on the vine foliage misericord of the 'trefoil' leaf which first appeared at the beginning of the fourteenth

PLATE 31 Misericord from Blagdon, Somerset with three
cloaked heads (cat. 79)

PLATE 32 Misericord from Blagdon, Somerset with vine
leaves and fruit (cat. 80)

century. Here is a good example of a country crafts-man being stylistically behind the times and a possible instance of the tendency to historicism in the fifteenth century.

87

MISERICORD, mutilated and decorated with modern polychromy, representing the Assumption of the Virgin; the Virgin in an auriole or vesica-shaped border borne up by angels, and beneath a kneeling monk (PL.33)
Said to come from Malmesbury Abbey
Formerly in the Maskell Collection
Mid 15th century
19.7 x 31.7 x 16 cm
377-1890
The scene is shown with the Virgin already crowned, and a kneeling monk, at the bottom left-hand side, who takes the place of St Thomas holding the Virgin's belt. Since the Virgin is crowned it is surprising that the figure of God the Father, or the Trinity, is not included above. Only two other versions of the subject survive on misericords, at Occold, Suffolk and Lincoln Cathedral (At Harlaxton, Lincs there is a misericord consisting of an upturned crown supported on either side by a hand).

In the last edition of the catalogue this item was not listed as a misericord but as a 'corbel' or 'bracket-like carving'. However, the previous owner was in no doubt as to its identity (Maskell 1911, PL.53, FIG.9). The piece has been crudely sawn all round and, at the bottom, the monk's sleeve and the angel's robe have been curtailed. At the top the mouldings of the bracket have been defaced so that any evidence for there having been supporters is missing. The characteristic profile of a misericord, with its rapidly diminishing depth from top to bottom is unmistakable.

The omission of the upper tier of figures usually present in representations of this subject is logical given the function of the carving. The V&A's alabaster panel of the second half of the fifteenth century (Acq.No.A.62-1946) displays a crowned Virgin surrounded by angels above which is a broad wavy ledge which supports God the Father flanked by angels (FIG.23). It has been suggested that the ledge represents heaven (Cheetham 1984, 205) and another example of its use has been cited on an alabaster panel in Ghent. At Malmesbury the misericord bracket probably suggested the ledge to the wood carver prompting him to concentrate exclusively on the figure of the

FIG 21 St Martin, Worle, Somerset. Misericord with vine foliage and fruit.

FIG 22 St Martin, Worle, Somerset. Misericord with two heads in a cloak.

Virgin with her attendants.

The depiction of the Virgin in a mandorla already crowned is not as common as examples showing her either uncrowned or in the act of being crowned. The iconographical parallels with the V&A's alabaster panel, already mentioned, can be supplemented with stylistic consonances. The handling of the draperies is very similar in both cases, particularly the flowing cloak of the Virgin. The belted tunics of the angels, gathered at the waist with broad collars at the neck are also close. The Virgin's hair style is the same, as well as the decorative patterning on the edge of the misericord and the thick ribs on the angel's wings.

The best match for the angels on the Malmesbury misericord is the pair on the end of the tomb of Sir John Cressy, d. 1444, at Dodford, Northants. The handling of the drapery and the wings is very

PLATE 33 Assumption of the Virgin misericord (cat. 87)

FIG 23 V & A Museum. Alabaster panel of 'Assumption of Virgin' (Acq. No. A. 62-1946).

similar and the heads are crowned with bands displaying crosses above the foreheads. Taking into account this comparison, and the stylistic parallels with the V&A's alabaster panel, a date for the misericord around the middle of the fifteenth century would not be unreasonable.

The survival of this misericord probably indicates that it was of some importance and may have come from one of the principal seats. These were usually given some special decorative embellishment. The liturgical choir at Malmesbury was under the crossing tower and in the first bay of the presbytery. The stalls themselves must have been of some pretension. We know that they had canopies since the structural evidence for them can still be seen (Brakspear 1913, 422). The choice of the 'Assumption of the Virgin' for a misericord was particularly apt because, in the tenth century the abbey dedicated in the seventh century to St Peter and St Paul, received a new dedication to St Aldhelm and the Blessed Virgin.

88

PINNACLE, carved in relief against a board with chamfered edges; at the top a crocketted finial above a moulded capital; the two tapered sides decorated with foliage crockets; at the base ogee-shaped arches forming a gable with trefoil cusping on the underside and moulded pendants below.
Late 15th century
8.4 x 8.9 x 12.3 cm
W.4-1930

89

CANOPY ARCH, from choir-stall, the curved sides decorated with leaf crockets, the interior having geometrical tracery with foliated cusps (PL.34).
About 1365
108 x 66 cm
W.21-1921

This fragment was formerly in the Royal Architectural Museum, Westminster (Architectural Museum 1877, 53, No.841). It is probably from the destroyed church of St Katherine-by-the-Tower, London (COL. PL.1). The royal hospital of St Katherine's-by-the-Tower was established under royal patronage in the twelfth century (Druce 1917). The building with which we are concerned was started in 1340 by William Erldesby, the master of the hospital and the queen's treasurer. The institution received a new charter in 1351 from Queen Philippa by which instrument it was generously endowed. Rebuilding was slow, and it was not finished when the queen died in 1369. Druce maintained that it was probably not until about the time of King Edward's death in 1377 that the new choir-stalls were eventually finished (Druce 1917, 4). The carving style of such of the furniture as survives, however, suggests a date in the mid 1360s for the manufacture of the stalls. Although only the seating remains, antiquarian records made before demolition in the early nineteenth century provide us with a reliable idea of the form of this furniture. It is the only surviving witness of mid fourteenth-century choir-stalls made under direct royal patronage. The two other fourteenth-century sets of metropolitan choir-stalls, at St Stephen's Chapel, Westminster and St George's Chapel, Windsor, are no longer extant.

The St Katherine's Hospital choir-stalls were moved in 1826 to a new building designed by Ambrose Poynter north of Cumberland Terrace, Regent's Park. This was damaged by bombing dur-

ing the Second World War. The seating of all the return and four of the lateral stalls was subsequently moved to the foundation's present home at Butcher Row, Stepney. There were originally twenty-four stalls in all.

Our knowledge of the superstructure is limited to various drawings, the earliest of 1780 by John Carter (See below for a list of some of the antiquarian records). From an examination of these there can be no doubt that the museum's fragment is reliably attributed. The canopies above the seats were flanked by buttresses. The apex of their arches broke through the line of the cornice above. Over the entrance to the choir were three large canopies of a more three-dimensional design.

The choir-stalls were of the conventional double-screen 'London' type, as exemplified in the lower portion of the work at Ely Cathedral, or the furniture at Wells Cathedral of the late 1330s, except that the gables were allowed to break free of the crowning cornice. It is unfortunate that there is such a big gap between these monuments and the St Katherine's Hospital furniture (Although the Gloucester Cathedral choir-stalls, of about 1350, seem to have been designed by a metropolitan artist, they must have been executed by West Country craftsmen [Tracy 1987, 44-48]). The foliage in the earlier furniture is far too naturalistic to show much continuity with that at St Katherine's. On the other hand, if we look forward a few years to the Lincoln Cathedral choir-stalls, of about 1370, the vocabulary of architectural and sculptural motifs betray the near contemporaneity of both monuments. The tracery of the gables on the upper tabernacles at Lincoln is very similar to that on the gables at St Katherine's with the combination of tear-drop and quatrefoil motifs familiar from the choir-stalls at Gloucester Cathedral. Some of the foliage on the gable crockets at Lincoln is also very close to that at St Katherine's as exemplified on the museum's gable and the surviving misericords. Also the way that the leaf crockets emerge from grooved 'plates' of wood on the gable can be paralleled at Lincoln. The conceit of recessing the spaces between the leaves of the voluted 'trefoil' kind of foliage in the shape of a dagger is found in both places. This pattern occurs where the leaves are distinctly separated. The motif can be traced back to 'London' work of the 1320s (See CAT.67 where this leaf form is found on the museum's misericord from Lincoln Cathedral and Tracy 1987, 49-55).

Note. Some antiquarian drawings of the St Katherine's choir-stalls:

PLATE 34 Canopy arch from St Katherine's-by-the-Tower (cat. 89)

JOHN CARTER. Watercolour. 1780 (Port of London Authority. COL. PL.1).
Sketched plans and details. 1775 (Guildhall Library, London).
Ink drawing of choir. 1780 (BL.Add.36402, f.44).
ANONYMOUS. Record made prior to demolition. 1826 (Formerly at Salmesbury Hall, Blackburn. Lost).

B. FERREY. Engraved elevation, section and detail of a canopy. Pugin 1831, St Katherine's Church, PL.I.
J.W. ARCHER. Drawing of choir interior. 1834. (BL. Dept of Prints and Portfolio XV).
E.M. BARRY INK sketch of stall canopy. 1849. (R.I.B.A. drawings coll. E.M. Barry Sketchbook).

PLATE 35 Boss from the Winchester Cathedral choir-stalls (cat. 90)

90

Boss, carved in openwork with a vine stem bearing leaves and grapes (PL.35).

From the Winchester Cathedral choir-stalls

1308-10

16.8 x 9.5 x 9.5 cm

236-1897

There were two distinctive but clearly related campaigns in the making of the choir-stalls at Winchester Cathedral. The original stalls were erected, and presumably designed, by William Lyngwode a Norfolk master-carver whose continued residence at Winchester was requested by the furniture's patron, Bishop Woodlock, in the summer of 1308 (and again the following year) in a surviving letter to Bishop Salmon of Norwich (A.Goodman 1927, 126). Sometime after this the stalls must have started to show the symptoms of imminent collapse which still can be seen today. A programme of renovation was put in hand by the same team of workmen who had made the original furniture and the work cannot have been finally completed much later than about 1315 (Tracy 1987, 16-24).

The museum's boss is part of the first campaign and comes from one of the canopies above a seat (FIG.24). There must have been sixty-six stalls originally, enough to accommodate the known number of monks at Winchester in 1325 together with the prior and sub-prior (Tracy 1987b). The lateral stalls were shortened by four seats, almost certainly, to accommodate the Inigo Jones choir-screen. A manuscript note by Thomas Wharton in his own copy of his *Description of Winchester* (1760) seems to confirm this (C.G. Wilson 1976, 16-18). This runs: 'Charles I ordered ... the present screen to be built 1637 and raise the Ascent by 2 or 3 steps so shorten-

FIG 24 Winchester Cathedral. Vaulting of choir-stall canopies. Detail.

ing the choir by two double seats'. As the seats in the Winchester choir-stalls are, uniquely, arranged in pairs the removal of two units would have reduced the seating capacity by four. The museum's boss must have been severed from the rest of the furniture at this time.

The sensitive semi-naturalistic carving to be found on the work of the first campaign with its distinctively 'humpy' Decorated style leaves is reflected in the treatment of the museum's boss. Other familiar characteristics such as the alternation of the inside and outside of a leaf and the prominent stalks with budded shoots can also be recognised. The repertory of leaf forms on the Winchester Cathedral choir-stalls is extensive. Six different types have been listed (Cave 1943, 4-5) but the hazel leaf which appears only on the misericords and a three-pointed leaf with irregularly-cut sharp edges should be added

91

PINNACLE, probably from the canopy of a choir stall, carved with crockets, and fixed to a buttress carved with tracery and surmounted by two half finials carved with leaf work.
Late 15th century
96.5 x 10.8 cm
152-1897
This fragment is from the Cottingham Collection. The style is not dissimilar to the woodwork in the Lady Chapel choir-stalls at Winchester Cathedral of 1486-92 (Bond Stalls, 72)

92

PINNACLE, consisting of a pentagonal gable intersected by mouldings carved with crockets, the flat surface being decorated with a chevron moulding. The polygonal base is composed of tracery on a moulded plinth with embattled cornice above. At the angles are four buttresses with finials. The pinnacle assembly is now in separate pieces.
About 1480
95.5 x 35.6 x 25.4 cm
W. 69-1929
From the choir-stalls in St George's Chapel, Windsor. In the original arrangement of the canopies spires alternated with towers. The former, which were comparatively low, crowned the canons' seats. The knight-companions sat under the towers (See Hope 1913, II, 433, FIG.34). which were surmounted by a crest and banner. Subsequently, many of the spired canopies were replaced by replicas of the towered variety. No doubt the museum's specimen, which answers exactly to the established pattern, is one that suffered this fate (there are several others preserved at Windsor).

The St George's Chapel choir-stalls are the earliest for which comprehensive accounts have survived. The canopies were made in London, the carvers being Robert Ellis and John Filles. They appear to have been Englishmen and their work is stylistically in the tradition of indigenous ecclesiastical joinery. The great rood, on the other hand, was made by craftsmen from the Low Countries (Hope 1913, II, 429-45)

93

UPPER PART of an ARCADING, possibly from a stall backing; composed of two arches carved with foliage and having a grotesque mask in the apex of each. Between, in the spandrels, are two roundels, each containing a seated figure in relief holding a scroll. One, which faces, and is apparently disputing or discussing with the other, probably represents a prophet, and the other an apostle; the prophet being represented wearing shoes and the apostle without them. The back of the arcading is completely undecorated, the whole being carved out of a solid piece of wood 8.9 cm thick. The top moulding is flat also with mortises (PL.36).
Probably from the Fens
Given by Mr Murray Adams-Acton, through the National Art-Collections Fund
About 1290-1320
36.8 x 155 cm

PLATE 36 Arcading fragment possibly from a stall backing (cat. 93)

W.3-1928

This fragment was probably part of the backing of a set of choir-stalls, the lack of decoration on the back implying that it must have been placed against a wall. The use of such figures in the spandrels suggests a location of some importance within the church and the choir-stalls seem to be the most plausible possibility. Medallions in the arcade spandrels and masks at the apex of the arches are rather unusual motifs in fourteenth-century woodwork, although cusped oculi are plentiful at Winchester Cathedral. There must have been animals infesting the cusps of the arches, judging from the residual feet still clinging to the mouldings.

The foliage in the mouldings is typical of the humpy early Decorated type as exemplified on the choir-stalls at Winchester (1308-10) and Chichester (c.1315) cathedrals. Two particular species are exhibited – ivy and oak. The third is a conventional trefoil. In the case of the ivy the leaves are placed fronts and backs side by side in the manner typical of this period. The drawing of the figures is similar to that in the Peterborough Psalter in Brussels (Bib.Roy.MS.9961-62) considered by one writer to be of the second decade of the fourteenth century (Sandler 1974, 108-11) but by others (See Bennett 1982, 508) of the late thirteenth century, particularly the handling of the drapery, the head types, and the use of the long-sleeved undergarment. The hat worn by the prophet with its rounded brim and top-knot can be matched exactly. The head type and hat of the Jewish elder can also be matched closely on the Jesse Cope in the V & A (175-1889)

FIG 25 V & A Museum. Jesse Cope. Detail (Acq. No. 175-1889).

(FIG.25). This embroidery was made sometime between 1295 and 1315 (King 1963, 21). The rather elongated faces placed at an angle with long noses and slanting eyes are comparable in both works. The placing of robed figures holding scrolls in pairs as if in conversation is reminiscent of the treatment of the ancestors of Christ in Tree of Jesse representations. The early fourteenth-century section of the De Lisle Psalter (BL.Arundel 83) provides a relevant example on folio 14.

PLATE 37 Portion of rood screen
from Tilbrook. Cambs (cat. 95)

SCREENS AND PANELS

94

PANEL, from a parclose screen in the north nave aisle
of the church of Great Barton, Suffolk, painted with
the Annunciation. The Virgin, nimbed and
wearing a blue mantel over a red robe decorated
with conventional flowers, stands beneath a
canopy with gold brocade back. On a desk on the
left is a scroll inscribed: *Ecce ancilla do[mini;]* on the
right is a kneeling figure of the donor, a Grey Friar,
named Michael, a scroll issuing from his mouth
inscribed: *Miseratrix a[n]i[m]e mychyll ab hoste protege.*
Above is a pot of lilies with a figure of Christ
crucified among the stems; above, again, is a figure
of the First Person of the Trinity in a rayed border;
near the head of the Virgin is the Dove; on the top
of the panel is an estuary or sea-shore with ships.
The floor is tiled. The face and hands of the Virgin
and the figures of the Persons of the Trinity have

been defaced (COL.PL.4).

Given by Mr A. H. Fass

Late 15th century

110 x 45.6 cm

W.50-1921

In the nineteenth century this panel was in the collection of Sir Henry Bunbury who removed it from Holy Innocents, Great Barton, Suffolk at some time before 1850 (S.I.A., I, 1850, 231).

In a short notice in *The Antiquaries Journal* (H. Smith 1921) it was suggested that the seascape in the spandrel at the top of the panel might indicate that the painting was made for the Franciscan house at Dunwich. Nicholas Rogers (in a letter to the museum in 1979) has suggested that the work is more likely to have been connected with the house at Babwell. He also claims that the panel is: 'undoubtedly a product of the Bury school, about 1470-90, and may have been painted by a member of the Albreed family'.

The motif of the crucifixion in this position is a characteristically English one (see Hildburgh 1923-4).

95

PORTION of a ROOD SCREEN, with traces of colour. Composed of a central pointed arch with openwork tracery in the spandrels, and the half of a similar arch on each side. The front of the loft above is an arcade with six arches, below which is a border of pierced quatrefoils (PL.37).

From Tilbrook Church, Cambridgeshire

Late 14th century

339 x 3.28 cm

W.82-1910

In the fifteenth century this fourteenth-century screen was reused as the eastern portion of the rood screen in Tilbrook Church. The remaining western part, which is still in position in the church, is illustrated in V.C.H., *Bedfordshire*, III, 172; and also in Colling 1848-50, II, PLS. 65, 66 and 69. On Plate 66 is a section of the screen showing the position of the portions now in the Museum (FIG.26).

Probably a screen in front of a narrow chancel arch with altars on each side. This is one of the earliest rood lofts of wood. The surviving fragments were probably from the front of the original screen, utilized as the back parapet when the later screen was erected. A somewhat similar front portion with an openwork parapet above the lower part of the fifteenth century exists at Milton Ernest, Beds, though now misplaced in the north aisle (V.C.H. *Bedfordshire*, III, 148).

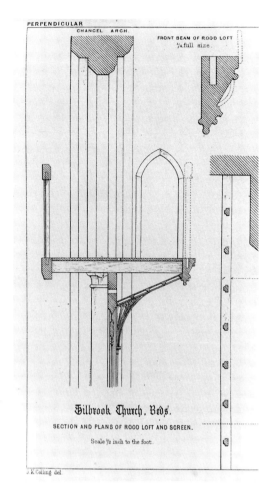

FIG 26 All Saints, Tilbrook, Cambridgeshire. Section of roodscreen (from J.K. Colling, *Gothic Ornaments*, London, 1850, II, Pl. 66).

96

PANEL from a screen, with three sunk quatrefoils with moulded borders, having a boss in the centre carved in openwork relief. The carvings represent: (1) a figure amidst foliage, (2) a figure with club on the back of a horned beast, (3) an animal amidst foliage (PL.38).

About 1370

23.8 x 70 cm

W.102-1924

Quatrefoiled panels are incorporated in the choir-stalls at Lincoln in the desk fronts of the sub-stalls (FIG.27). Most of them were replaced with modern imitations by Pearson when the furniture was restored in the late nineteenth century. The museum was given one of these at the same time as the medieval panel was acquired. This second panel (W.103-1924) was described as fourteenth-century in the previous catalogue (Smith 1929, 31). However, it must have been accepted by the museum as an example of nineteenth-century craftsmanship. In-

PLATE 38 Panel with sunk quatrefoils from Lincoln
Cathedral. (cat. 96)

FIG 27 Lincoln Cathedral. Choir desk front. Detail.

terestingly, the modern panel was not made from
one piece of wood, as is the case in the few surviving authentic examples, and it has come apart at
the join.

This panel's medieval credentials are confirmed
by the battered condition of the carving and by the
choice of leaf used in the spandrels. The foliage is an
adaptation of the rosette, the common motif used
in this furniture. The museum's carving compares
well with the authentic medieval panel, in very
much better condition, in the south-west corner of
the sub-stalls. The spandrel carvings are not identical but the expanded rosette motif with its button-
like stamen is clearly recognisable in both.

The foliage used in the left hand quatrefoil of the
museum's panel is oak leaf, one of the seven species
used on the choir-stalls. Another figure of a woodwose entangled in an oak thicket can be seen on a
misericord in the cathedral.

The date of the erection of the stalls at Lincoln is
c.1370 (See CAT.67).

97
PORTION of a SCREEN, consisting of a pair of doors,
together forming an arch; the lower part of each
door is enclosed by panels decorated with applied
tracery, the upper part has two open lights
separated by a shaft into compartments headed by
cusped and moulded tracery. Fitted with iron
hinges and latch. The surface of the wood covered

PLATE 39 Two pairs of screen doors from a Devon church (cat. 97 & 98)

with brown paint. Typical of the screenwork of the district round Exeter (PL.39).

From a Devonshire church

Late 15th century

193 x 96.5 x 11.8 cm

118-1865

These must have been the doors of a rood-screen which was probably fan-vaulted. See CAT.99.

98

PORTION of a SCREEN, consisting of a pair of doors with square tops; the lower part of each door is enclosed by two carved panels, the upper part has three lights separated by shafts into compartments headed by cusped and moulded tracery. The doors have been altered and the framework has been partly renewed (PL.39).

From a Devonshire church

Late 15th or early 16th century

Each door, 211 x 54.5 x 11.8 cm

118A-1865

These must have been the doors of a parclose screen quite probably from the same church as CAT.97.

99

FRAGMENTS of OPENWORK TRACERY, nineteen, from a screen.

From a Devonshire church

Late 15th or early 16th century

Various sizes

118B-1865

These fragments are from the same source as Nos. 97 and 98. The coating of brown paint was removed from some of them, and revealed traces of the original colour.

100-101

TWO PANELS, from a rood screen, each painted with two full length, nimbed figures of saints, in gold and colours.

1. St Leonard, tonsured, in a black robe, with crosier

FIG 28 St Michael, Barton Turf, Norfolk. Figure of St Apollonia from rood-screen.

and manacles; St Agnes (?St Katherine), in ermine-lined red mantle over a green and blue under-robe, with sword and book.

2. St Agatha, in blue ermine-lined red mantle over a green robe, with pincers in her left hand holding a breast. St William of Norwich, in a red mantle over a brown robe, with bare feet, three nails in his head, three nails in the right hand, and a hammer in the left.

The backgrounds to each figure are alternately red and green, St Leonard being on red, and are decorated with pomegranate and flower patterns in gold. The paintings have been restored (COL.PLS.5&6).

About 1450-70

Each panel, 102 x 74.6 cm, on oak

23 and 24-1894

These panels come from the Chapel of St Mary in the church of St John Maddermarket, Norwich. Above Sts Leonard and William is the device, and above Sts Agatha and Apollonia, the initials of Ralf Segrym, merchant of Norwich, the donor of the panels. He was Sheriff in 1447, M.P. in 1449, and Mayor in 1451. St William of Norwich, child martyr, was said to have been strangled and crucified in 1144 by Jews. His body was discovered some years afterwards in a wood, as the result of his appearance to a dying man. It was buried with great honour, and the grave became the scene of many miracles.

Nicholas Rogers points out that: 'Several writers, such as Constable (1929, I, 141) and Rickert (1965, 187 & PL.189), assume that these panels are datable to 1451, the year when Segrym was mayor. However, Ralph Segrym did not die until 1472, and his wife Agnes until 1474 (Norwich, D.P.R., 81, 82 Gelour). ... a date in the 1450's or 60's is likely given the similarities with the main screen at Barton Turf, Norfolk. Decorative motifs such as background patterns and haloes in the two places are comparable, St Agatha resembles the Barton Turf St Apollonia (FIG.28), and a slightly harder version of St William's facial type is provided by the Barton Turf St Barbara'.

Rogers favours the identification of the second figure as St Katherine. To support this he adduces the turban worn by St Katherine at Walpole St Peter.

102

FOUR PANELS, the lower part of a rood screen, painted in oils and gilt, within a framework carved with conventional Gothic foliage and set in cusped arches of ogee form. They represent the Adoration of the Magi, arranged as a continuous composition;

FIG 29 St Peter, Buckland-in-the-Moor, Devon. Adoration of the Magi panel from rood-screen.

from left to right: (1) The Virgin seated holding the Infant Christ. (2) The Magi kneeling and offering a cup with his crown before him on the ground. (3) Another of the Magi. (4) The Moorish King. Above the arches trefoils painted alternately red and green, below four quatrefoils, similarly treated, each containing carved foliage gilt (COL.PL.7).
West Country
About 1520
Given by Viscount Lascelles
94 x 115 x 14.6 cm
W.54-1928
These panels were discussed in a notice by Borenius and Tristram (Borenius 1928, 125-26) who pointed out that the composition closely resembles representations of the same subject on the rood screens at Plymtree and Buckland-in-the-Moor, Devon.

The treatment of a composition in a frieze-like manner where the action of one figure follows on from another occurs only rarely on East Anglian screens. But in Devon it is characteristic. The 'Adoration of the Magi' can be found in three surviving Devon screens, at Buckland-in-the-Moor, Plymtree and Ugborough. The composition at Buckland is very close to that on the museum's panels (FIG.29). In the screen at Plymtree the scheme is again similar, although the crown on the ground

in front of the first king is omitted and the frankincense container in the right hand figure is not boat-shaped. According to Keyser the treatment of the subject at Ugborough is also close (Keyser 1883, 199). An indirect but recognisable stylistic debt to the figure sculpture on the west-front of Exeter Cathedral has been adduced for this group of late Gothic panel painting in Devon (Constable 1928).

103
TWO PANELS, from a screen, painted in colours within a framework (partly restored), surmounted by cusped arches, painted and gilt. On the left, standing on a pedestal, is a nun with halo, holding a closed book in her left hand; the red ground sprinkled with rosettes, alternately gilt. On the right, on a similar pedestal, stands St. Helen with crown and halo, wearing a scarlet cloak, and holding a closed book in her left hand and a small tau-shaped cross in her right; the dark green ground with rosettes, as before (COL.PL.8).
From Tatterford Church, Norfolk
Given by Mr J. H. Fitzhenry
Late 15th century
106 x 60 cm
271-1906

104

PANELLING, from the lower part of a screen, painted in colours. It is divided by mouldings into eight panels surmounted by cusped arches, each subdivided above into two similar arches; the panels painted alternately red and green and stencilled with conventional floral patterns in white; one buttress painted with tracery remains, the others are missing; the openwork tracery along the bottom of the panelling is also missing (PL.40). From West Stow Church, Suffolk
Given by Mr A. H. Fass
First quarter 15th century
108 x 169 cm
W.149-1921
On arrival at the Museum the panelling was wholly covered with white paint, the removal of which revealed the original colours.

105

FRAGMENT of CRESTING from a screen carved in openwork with a foliated trefoil and a portion of another below which is a smaller trefoil and half of another. The lower part of the cresting is moulded.
Given by Mr Martin Travers
15th century
22.2 x 18.4 cm
W.108-1924
Purchased by the donor in Norwich, this fragment is from a Norfolk church.

106

FRAGMENT of CRESTING, from a screen, carved in openwork with a foliated trefoil.
Given by Mr Martin Travers
15th century
10.4 x 7.6 cm
W.109-1924
Purchased by the donor in Norwich, this fragment is from a Norfolk church.

PLATE 41 Frieze of cornice from Zeal Monachorum, Devon (cat. 109)

107
CRESTING, carved in openwork with a band of upright trefoils, the alternate trefoils, which are larger and more elaborate, united above by a circular rod.
Given by Mr F. C. Eeles
15th century
20.3 x 86.5 cm
W. 420-1922
From a church in North Oxfordshire.

108
FRIEZE or CORNICE, from a screen carved with quatrefoils and surmounted by a moulding.
Given by Mr A. H. Fass
15th century
26.7 x 183 cm
W.148-1921
From a Suffolk church.

109
FRIEZE or CORNICE, pierced and carved with a band of vine leaves (PL.41).
Given by Mr William Bailey
Early 16th century
12.7 x 94 cm
W.412-1922
Said to have come from Zeal Monachorum Church, Devon

110
CRESTING, from a screen, pierced and carved with six foliated trefoils.
Given Mr by Frank Jennings
15th century
10.8 x 42.8 cm
W.23-1924
From a Suffolk church.

111
CRESTING, from a screen, pierced and carved with seven foliated trefoils.
Given by Mr Frank Jennings
15th century
6.5 x 29.9 cm
W.26-1924
From a Suffolk church.

112
ARCH MOULDING, a crocketted ogee arch from the tracery of a screen; carved with a twisted cable and two crockets in the form of flowers with stamens.
Given by Mr Frank Jennings
15th century
54.6 x 6.50 cm
W.14-1924
From a Suffolk church.

113
ARCH MOULDING, a crocketted ogee arch from the tracery of a screen, gilt and carved with flowers.
Given by Mr Frank Jennings
15th century
49.5 x 9.1 cm
W. 15-1924
From a Suffolk church.

114
ARCH MOULDING a crocketted ogee arch from the tracery of a screen.
Given by Mr Frank Jennings
15th century
44.2 x 7.8 cm
W.16-1924
From a Suffolk church.

PLATE 42 Figure of an angel. East Anglia (cat. 121)

115
A FRAGMENT of an ARCH MOULDING, a crocketted ogee arch from the tracery of a screen, carved with a leaf pattern.
Given by Mr Frank Jennings
14th century
24.1 x 12.7 cm
W.18-1924
From a Suffolk church.

116
TRACERY ARCH, from a church screen, consisting of the upper part of one of the main arches, with its mouldings and perpendicular tracery (half the tracery missing). The woodwork retains considerable traces of its original colour and gilding.

Given by Mr A. L. Radford, F.S.A.
Late 15th century
53.4 x 61 cm
W.191-1923
From Devonshire (probably the Exe Valley). See also CAT.117.

117
BOSS, from a church screen; of oak, carved and gilt.
Given by Mr A. L. Radford, F.S.A.
Late 15th century
14.0 x 12.7 cm
W.195-1923
From Devon (probably the Exe Valley). From the intersection of the vaulting of the same screen as CAT.116.

PLATE 43 Tracery head from a Somerset church (cat. 123)

118
UPRIGHT of a Screen, with remains of paint. In the middle is a slightly projecting column, with a groove above; on each side is a band of leaf ornament wound round a central rod. The back is similarly treated, except that a projecting moulding takes the place of the column.
Given by Mr T. Charbonnier
Early 16th century
160 x 14 cm
198-1908
From a Devon church.

119
PORTION of MOULDED BEAM, from a screen, with remains of the original red and blue colour.
From Leigh Church, Wilts
Given by Rev. M. J. Milling
15th century
150 x 12.7 x 11.4 cm
W.12-1918

120
PORTION of a TURNED CAPITAL, probably from a screen.
Given by the Architectural Association
13th century
12.1 x 14 x 11 cm
W.20-1916
Formerly in the Royal Architectural Museum, Westminster (Architectural Museum, 54, No.904).

121
FIGURE of an angel, probably from a screen, half-length, with curly hair and feathers on body and arms, short cape on shoulders; the arms are raised (PL.42).
East Anglian
Given by the Architectural Association
15th century
22.2 x 24.1 cm
W.19-1916
Formerly in the Royal Architectural Museum, Westminster (Architectural Museum 1877, 54, No.858).

122
TRACERY HEAD, from a screen, carved on both sides in open work with one cusped arch and a portion of another.
From a church in North Oxfordshire
Given by Mr F. C. Eeles
Late 14th century
19 x 47 x 4.4 cm
W.419-1922
Purchased by the donor at Banbury.

123
TRACERY, from the opening of a screen, consisting of the head of an arch filled in with tracery. The whole has been painted in colours, now much destroyed, and there are traces of gilding (PL.43).
From a Somerset church
Late 15th century
30.5 x 98 cm
511-1893

PLATE 44 Tracery head from a Suffolk church (cat. 126)

124
TRACERY, from the opening of a screen, with arched top subdivided into two arches each carved with tracery, the cusps terminating in lobes and trefoils. With remains of colour and gilding.
Probably from Steeple Aston church, Oxon
Given by Rev. F. Meyrick Jones
Early 16th century
35.5 x 94 cm
W.534-1922

125
TRACERY (fragment), from a screen, in the form of a spandrel, with original colour and gilding.
West Country
Given by Rev. F. Meyrick Jones
15th century
28 x 8.9 cm
W.535-1922
Purchased by the donor at Taunton.

126
TRACERY HEADS, two fragments, from a screen, carved in open work and with foliations in the spandrels; with remains of red and green colour and gilding (PL.44).
From a Suffolk church
Given by Mr A. H. Fass
First half of 15th century
28 x 61 cm
W.151-1921
The original gold and colours were found under a coating of brown paint.

127
TRACERY HEAD, from a screen, carved in openwork with a cusped arch subdivided into two arches below; the spandrels each contain the figure of a bird gilded; the tracery has remains of the original red and green colour (PL.45).
From a Suffolk church
Given by Mr Frank Jennings
Late 15th century
25.4 x 50.8 cm
W.413-1922

128
TRACERY HEAD, from a screen, carved in openwork with three foiled and cusped arches (PL.46).
Probably Suffolk
First half of 15th century
21.7 x 61 cm
W.23-1921
Formerly in the Royal Architectural Museum, Westminster.

129
TRACERY HEAD, formed of four arches, each subdivided into two cusped arches and filled with pinnacles carved with foliated crockets.
Given by the Architectural Association
15th century
24.1 x 98 cm
W.12-1916
Formerly in the Royal Architectural Museum, Westminster (Architectural Museum 1877, 554, No. 857).

PLATE 45 Tracery head from a Suffolk church (cat. 127)

PLATE 46 Tracery head from Suffolk (cat. 128)

PLATE 47 Tracery heads from a Suffolk church (cat. 131)

130
TRACERY HEAD, formed of two arches with cusped heads, the spandrels filled with foliage.
Given by the Architectural Association
15th century
28 x 82.5 cm
W.13-1916
Formerly in the Royal Architectural Museum, Westminster (Architectural Museum 1877, 53, No.809).

131
TRACERY HEADS, two, each carved with a pair of arches with foliated cusps and carved foliations in the spandrels (PL.47).
From a Suffolk church.
Given by Mr A. H. Fass
About 1500
21.6 x 81.2 x 86.4 cm
W.150 and W.150A-1921

132
TRACERY HEADS, two, each carved in openwork with two arches, the cusps terminating with foliations-in one case with a lion mask, the spandrels carved with foliations and grotesque beasts and birds.
East Anglian
First half of 15th century
19 x 61 cm
W.24 and W.24A-1921
Formerly in the Royal Architectural Museum, Westminster.

133
TRACERY HEAD, consisting of three arches and portion of a fourth filled with geometrical tracery.
Suffolk
14th century

26 x 92 cm
W.12-1924
*Note.*Numbers W. 5, 6, 7, 9, 10 & 12-1924 were purchased from the Frank Jennings Collection. See also entries below.

134
TRACERY PANEL a fragment in two pieces, from a screen, carved on both sides. It consists of three arches and part of a fourth filled with geometrical tracery (PL.48).
From a Suffolk church
Late 14th century
34.2 x 33 x 2.87 cm
W.6-1924

135
TRACERY PANEL, with solid back, from a screen. It consists of one arch and portion of another. The spandrels are filled with quatrefoils, and in the centre compartment of the complete arch is a carved finial (PL.49).
From a Suffolk church
15th century
28 x 25.4 x 2.61 cm
W.7-1924

136
TRACERY PANEL, painted red; from a screen. It consists of two arches, each carved with three quatrefoils having flowers in the centre; in the spandrels are conventional leafage.
From a Suffolk church
15th century
27 x 65.5 cm
W.9-1924
Formerly in the Royal Architectural Museum, Westminster (Architectural Museum 1877, 53, No.809).

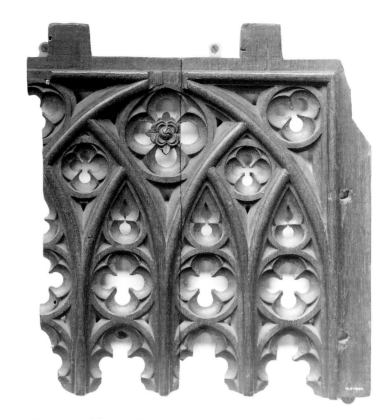

PLATE 49 Tracery panel from a Suffolk church (cat. 135)　　　PLATE 48 Tracery panel from a Suffolk church (cat. 134)

137
TRACERY PANEL, from the base of a screen, oblong,
painted yellow with traces of red. It consists of two
traceried quatrefoils centring in flowers, flanked by
single lancets.
From a Suffolk church
15th century
21.6 x 64.6 x 2.54 cm
W.10-1924

138
TRACERY PANEL, a fragment in two pieces, from a
screen, carved on both sides. The spandrels are
filled with acorns and oak leaves (PL.50).
From a Suffolk church
Late 15th century
43.2 x 56.6 x 2.6 cm
W.5-1924

139
TRACERY PANEL, carved with a quatrefoil in centre
and trefoils in the spandrels; repainted at a later
date (PL.51).
From a Suffolk church
Late 15th century
25.4 x 71.2 x 3.2 cm
W.11-1924

140
TRACERY (four fragments) originally applied to
panelling, probably of a screen carved with cusped
and crocketted arches and with floral designs in the
spandrels.
From a Suffolk church
Given by Mr Frank Jennings
15th century
Average 25.4 x 45.7 cm
W.27 to W.30-1924

141
TRACERY PANEL, from a screen, carved in openwork
with a quatrefoil within a lozenge, in the centre of
the quatrefoil a 'water flower' and foliage.
Norfolk
Given by Mr Martin Travers
15th century
22.8 x 24.2 cm
W.110-1924
Purchased by the donor in Norwich.

142
TRACERY HEAD, from base of a parclose screen;
painted red. From a Devonshire church.
Given by Mr A. L. Radford, F.S.A.
Late 15th century
48.2 x 20.3 x 3.3 cm
W.187-1923

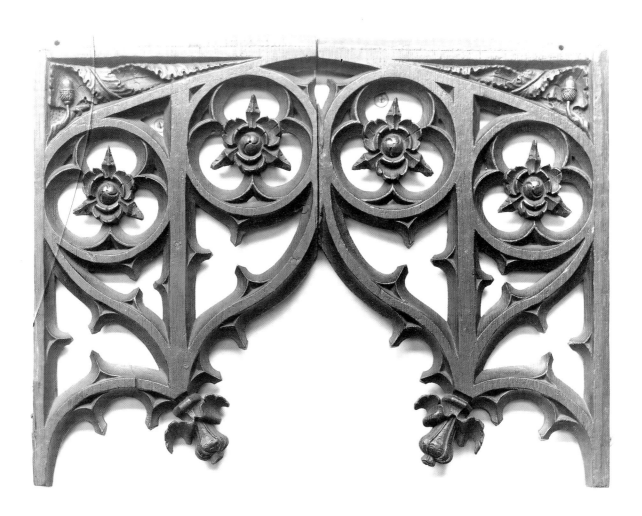

PLATE 50 Tracery panel from a Suffolk church (cat. 138)

PLATE 51 Tracery panel from a Suffolk church (cat. 139)

143
TRACERY HEAD, from dado panels of a screen,
consisting of a fragment of the arch moulding and a
spandrel with trefoil opening.
From a Devonshire church
Given by Mr A. L. Radford, F.S.A.
Early 16th century
20.3 x 33 x 3.2 cm
W.188-1923

144
TRACERY HEAD; portion of the dado panels of a
screen. It consists of an ogee headed arch with
quatrefoils and Gothic foliage above. From a
Devonshire church
Given by Mr A. L. Radford, F.S.A.
Late 15th century
28 x 41.9 cm
W.189-1923

145
TRACERY HEAD; from the dado panels of a church
screen. It is painted red and gilt, and consists of one
cusped ogee headed arch and portion of another,
with trefoils in the head.
From a Devonshire church
Given by Mr A. L. Radford, F.S.A.
Late 15th century
28 x 45.8 cm
W.190-1923

146
TRACERY HEAD; consisting of a pair of cusped arches
surmounted by eight single lights.
15th century
24.1 x 39.4 cm
Circ.64-1921

147
TRACERY HEAD; consisting of a cusped trefoil-
headed arch with pierced trefoils and triangles in
the spandrels.
15th century
22.9 x 39.4 cm
Circ.76-1921

148
PORTION OF ARCADING; pierced with two cusped
arches; the spandrels carved with leaf ornament.
Given by Mr Herbert Hutchinson
15th century
12.1 x 44.4 cm
499-1898

PLATE 52 Panel carved with sacred monogram (cat. 149)

149
PANEL; with decoration carved in low relief; the
shape is that of a straight-topped heraldic shield; the
top is edged with a border of embattled cresting;
below, in the middle of the shield, is the
monogram IHS in gothic characters; the I
terminates below in a trefoil stem and the H
terminates both above and below in two leaves on
stems; on either side of the monogram, and above
it, are three peg-holes, the upper hole still filled
with part of a wood peg, with the impress of
applied ornaments (PL.52).
Given by Dr Philip Nelson
c.1430
34.1 x 29.2 x 2.54 cm
W.10-1936
Probably one of the panels at the base of a screen or
one of a series spaced at intervals along a cornice.
The applied ornaments may have been Instruments
of the Passion since there seems already to be a nail
incorporated within the design of the S. The panel
is said to have come from Whalley Abbey, Lancs.
The trefoil termination of the I in the form of three
pellets is very like the crocket terminations
throughout the choir-stalls at Whalley (FIG.30). The
furniture was made during the abbacy of William
of Whalley (1418-34).

FIG 30 Whalley Abbey, Lancashire. Choir-stalls. Detail.

150
PANEL; incorporating two rows of arcading and
cusped arch at the base (PL.53).
15th century
51.1 x 43.8 cm
Circ.99-1920

151
TRACERY HEAD; consisting of four pierced
quatrefoils with foliated centres.
15th century
20.3 x 83 cm
Circ.216-1910

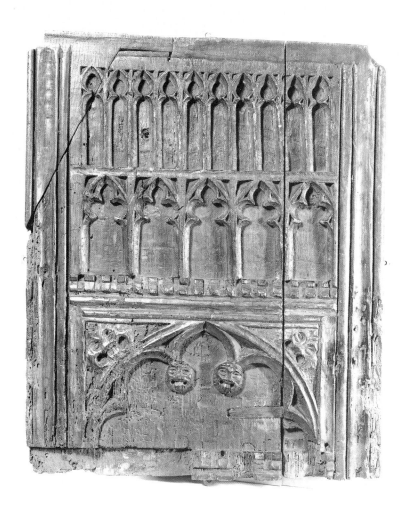

PLATE 53 Arcaded panel (cat. 150)

152
TRACERY HEAD; consisting of a pair of arches with
foliated spandrels.
15th century
20.3 x 83 cm
Circ.67-1921

153
TRACERY HEAD; with traces of colour; consisting of
three open pointed arches (two broken) each
decorated with four enriched cusps; the spandrels
of the left and central arches are filled with flowers

and leaves.
Late 15th century
26.7 x 132 cm
1970-1900

154
ARCH; decorated with openwork cusping; each
spandrel filled with a flower and leaves.
c.1500
1972, 19.7 x 36.2 cm, 1972A, 17.5 x 34.8 cm
1972 & 1972A-1900
From Sutton Place, Guildford.

PLATE 54 Last Judgement panel (cat. 157)

155

Tracery Head; two pieces, each carved in openwork with two arches having cusps terminating with foliations (in one case with a lion mask), the spandrels carved with foliations and grotesque beasts and birds.
15th century
19 x 61 cm
24 and 24A-1921

156

Frieze Fragment; decorated with openwork vine trail ornament.
Second half 15th century
50 x 11.4 cm
W.74-1929

157

Carved Panel; of square form, carved in high relief with a representation of the Last Judgement; Christ is seated in an attitude of blessing on a rainbow arch and flanked on the right by four prophetic figures among cloud scrolls, and on the left by two similar figures and a crowned figure. Below the arch are two converging figures of trumpeting angels, above nine small human figures, mostly nude. The Elect, on the left, are rising up. The Damned, on the right, are falling into Hell (PL.54).
Third quarter 15th century
24 x 22.5 x 8.5 cm
W.63-1938
Christ is shown with his cloak open at the chest to display his wounds. Behind him are the lily and the sword to indicate the place of the damned and the elect. On either side sit the assessors amongst whom is a figure with a crown on her head, probably intended for the Virgin.

A convincing treatment of the Last Judgement in wood survives only once, on a misericord at Sherborne Abbey, Dorset (FIG.31). But in that case there is only Christ seated on a rainbow, with no assessors.

The artist of the museum's carving chooses to depict more assessors than is usual in a work on such a small scale. In a fifteenth-century English alabaster in a private collection in Holland there are only four assessors. However, very often, only the Virgin and St John appeared, as on the mid fifteenth-century roof boss in St Peter, Hungate, Norwich. The cone-shaped trumpets of the angels are similar to a pair in the fifteenth-century English alabaster at Rouen (Cochet 1875, 80, No.71).

Unfortunately it is difficult to say much about the carving style since the surface is very rubbed. The date of manufacture must be sometime in the fifteenth century.

Perhaps the most interesting problem in connection with this piece is its original function. It is said to have come from a church in Lincolnshire and it has always been referred to as a roof boss. However, the church cannot be identified, and the scale and treatment of the carving rule out the roof boss hypothesis. The perspective implies that the composition was intended to be viewed from below in a vertical position. The sides, and particularly the top, which has an uneven profile, do not suggest that it was ever contained within a framework. The panel could have been one of a series intended to

FIG 31 Sherborne Abbey, Dorset. Last Judgement misericord.

FIG 32 St George's Chapel, Windsor. Last Judgement panel on desk front.

FIG 33 Private Collection. Coronation of the Virgin panel.

be hung on the back of a set of choir-stalls as at Winchester Cathedral in the fourteenth century. In the fifteenth-century St George's Chapel, Windsor choir-stalls figurative panels incorporated in the desk-fronts include a representation of the Last Judgement of sophisticated composition with two angel trumpeters leaning out of the picture (FIG.32). It has to be said that, by comparison, the museum's panel is relatively weak in design with the figure of Christ too small and balanced rather precariously on the rainbow. Even the Sherborne carving works better as a design. Another possibility is that the panel was part of the embellishment of the loft of a rood-screen. This hypothesis cannot be proved one way or another due to the virtually total disappearance of such lofts. A panel of similar size and date depicting the Coronation of the Virgin in a private collection may well have had a similar function to the museum's panel (FIG.33).

Dating this sculpture is difficult. The Sherborne (about 1440) and Windsor (about 1480, see Remnant 1969, 38 and CAT.92) choir-stalls are separated by some forty years. The relative bulkiness of the drapery on the museum's panel suggests a date nearer Windsor than Sherborne.

158-183
STALL or BENCH-ENDS, twenty-six, mostly
fragmentary. From the chancel and nave of
St Nicholas Chapel, King's Lynn. About 1419.
W.2 to W.11-1916; W.14, W.16 to W.18, W.20;
W.56 to W.60-1921; Circ.26, Circ.36 to 39, Circ.41-
1921
Nos. W. 2, 3, and 5 to 11-1916 were presented by the
Architectural Association; the others were purchased. For the history of these carvings, see Misericords (CAT.73 to 78). Some of the fragments are
recorded in the catalogue of the Royal Architectural Museum, Westminster, published in 1877.

158
PORTION of a STALL-END, carved in low relief. A
two-masted vessel of the 15th century, used for
fighting and trading purposes, is represented
moored or at anchor. It is square-rigged on the
main mast and lateen-rigged on the mizen; the
bowsprit is indistinct, the wood at this point having
probably been mutilated. The sails are furled and
there are pennons on the ends of the main yard, on
the top of the main mast, and on the bowsprit. The
forecastle, fighting tops, and after castle are clearly
shown, and on the latter can be seen the shields of
the knights. Other details indicated are the main
stay, shrouds and ratlines, lifts, sheets, gaskets,
bowlines, rudder, and a sheave of darts in the main
fighting top. In the sky the sun is shining from
beneath the clouds; on the opposite side are six
stars and a crescent moon; below in the sea are
fishes and a crab. The upper part of the panel,
which is incurved, is pierced with tracery and
surmounted by a figure of an angel (PL.55).
95 x 28 cm
W.16-1921
See Architectural Museum (1877), 52, No. 747. Ships
are also featured on early sixteenth-century bench-
ends at Bishops Lydeard, Somerset (FIG.34), and Bud-
leigh, Devon. Another prosperous port at Tiverton,
Devon displays a fleet merchantman on the exterior of its early sixteenth-century church (B.O.E.,
South Devon, 283-84).

159
PORTION of a STALL-END, carved in low relief. On the
upper part a ship of the type in use about 1400 is
shown becalmed. It is a single-masted vessel
showing fore and after-castles, fighting top, parral,
yard with square sail, sheets, and rudder. The lines

on the sail are probably folds, and two fenders are
indicated at the sides of the hull. The figure of a
man is shown on board. As a background to the
ship and on the lower part of the panel is some
Gothic tracery, while in the intervening space three
dried fish are shown. The sloping top of the panel is
decorated with two crockets (PL.56).
86.4 x 16.5 cm
W.6-1916
See Architectural Museum (1877), 52, No. 766. Compare CAT.158. The representation here of the split
fish is of historical interest, for the fisheries of King's
Lynn have always been of considerable importance,
and were supported from early times by a succes-
sion of royal charters (see H. Smith 1925).

FIG 34 St Mary, Bishop's Lydeard, Somerset. Bench-end
with ship.

PLATE 55 Portion of a stall-end from St Nicholas, King's Lynn, displaying two-masted ship (cat. 158)

PLATE 56 Portion of a stall-end from St Nicholas, King's Lynn, displaying single-masted ship (cat. 159)

160

STALL- or BENCH-END, with foliated poppy-head
(broken), and on the elbow-rest a grotesque figure
with hoofed feet; the head and shoulders covered
with a hood (PL.57).

109 x 42 cm

W.3-1916

See Architectural Museum (1877), 53, No.791. This
style of bench-end, with a figure surmounting the
buttress extension is the most characteristic from
King's Lynn. It can be seen in the late fourteenth-
century furniture at Walpole St Peter, Norfolk, and
in the woodwork at St Mary, Bury St Edmund's,
Suffolk of *c*.1440. At Bury the repertory of beasts is
similar to that at King's Lynn including the collared
yale (See FIG. 36 & CAT.161).

161-166

FIVE PORTIONS of STALL-ENDS, forming elbow-rests.
From St Nicholas Chapel, King's Lynn

161

A gorged yale (PL.58).

61 x 16.5 cm

W.5-1916

Another almost identical animal, but unspotted, is
still *in situ* on a desk-end at St Nicholas. The yale is a
heraldic antelope: it has horns and a large pair of
projecting tusks (See Druce 1911). Its colouring is
silver bezanty, that is, white with yellow spots. It is
one of the supporters on the arms of the Dukes of
Somerset and appears on the stall plate of Sir John
Beaufort at St George's Chapel, Windsor. Sir John
was created Knight of the Garter about 1440 (Hope
1901, PL.LVIII). It also appears in various positions on
the Henry V Chantry at Westminster Abbey. Henry died in 1422 but it is probable that the chantry
was not completed for another twenty years
(Druce 1911, 188). Although our animal lacks the
prominent tusks it has awesome teeth. The unspotted yale at St Nicholas has unmistakable tusks in its
lower jaw (Tusks were not a mandatory attribute
of a heraldic yale). The gouges on the museum's
beast's body seem to be intended to represent the
spots of gold. On the Windsor stall plate there is a
pair of golden horns, and a flourishing mane and tail
(Druce 1911, PL.I, NO.2). On the museum's King's
Lynn carving the horns are ribbed as they are at
Windsor. There is a slight indication of a mane. The
heraldic origins of this beast are emphasized by the
gorging.

   A gorged and chained, but unspotted, yale, with
prominent tusks close in style to the King's Lynn

PLATE 57 Stall- or bench-end from St Nicholas, King's Lynn,
with hooded figure (cat. 160)

FIG 35 Wiggenhall St German's, Norfolk. Bench-end with yale.

beasts is found at Wiggenhall St German's (FIG.35), Chesterton and Feltwell, Norfolk, St Mary, Bury St Edmund's (FIG.36) where the animal is punched with spots, and Ufford, Suffolk, and Boston, Lincs (FIG.37). From the frequency of its occurrences in East Anglia, at least, it is clear that the yale was a popular subject for the woodcarver. There is no evidence whatsoever of any connection between the rebuilding of St Nicholas, King's Lynn, and the Beaufort family. On the contrary, the citizens were proud of the fact that they had raised the funds for the rebuilding themselves (Beloe 1900, 149-51). Moreover, the arms of the town was emblazoned on one of the poppy heads (CAT.167).

PLATE 58 Fragment of a stall- or bench-end from St Nicholas, King's Lynn, displaying gorged yale (cat. 161)

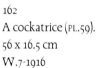

PLATE 59 Fragment of a stall- or bench-end from St Nicholas, King's Lynn, displaying a cockatrice (cat. 162)

FIG 36 St Mary, Bury St Edmund's, Suffolk. Yale on bench-end.

162
A cockatrice (PL.59).
56 x 16.5 cm
W.7-1916
See Architectural Museum (1877), 52, No. 756. The gouging technique required for indicating the white speckles of this cockatrice was favoured by the King's Lynn sculptor. It can be seen on other figures in the museum's collection from the church (W.10, W.59 & W.60-1921). A comparable cockatrice can be seen on a bench-end at Stonham Aspall (FIG.38) and on a misericord at Stowlangtoft, Suffolk. The treatment of the wings is similar to that on the buttress figure on W.9-1916 (CAT.164).

163
A mantichora with a bearded head (PL.60).
40.7 x 24.2 cm
W.8-1916
See Architectural Museum (1877), 53, No. 785.

164
A semi-detached column surmounted by a winged figure (PL.61).
68.5 x 15.3 cm
W.9-1916
The moulding on the shoulder and the treatment of the figure surmounting the buttress on this bench-end fragment seems to conform to the style of the other St Nicholas woodwork. Judging from the shape of the mortise on the side the piece formed the end of a desk in front of a set of congregational benching or choir-stalls.

This is the only known occurrence of the motif of a detached column on a desk or bench-end in East Anglia. The idea is usually associated with joinery of the late fifteenth- and early sixteenth centuries in the north of England where it is a standard feature of the 'Ripon School' of ecclesiastical furniture (Purvis 1929 & 1935). The playful idea of a column rising up through little miniature roofs can be found in East Anglia as at Wiggenhall St German's, Norfolk, and Fressingfield, Suffolk. In the latter case a complete detachment of the buttresses is

FIG 37 St Botolph, Boston. Yale on choir-stalls.

FIG 38 St Mary, Stonham Aspall, Suffolk. Bench-end with cockatrice.

unequivocally implied by the design.

The appearance of the detached buttress at this time is certainly surprising and it is particularly useful to have a provenance for it with a reliable date.It is possible that there were many more East Anglian examples from the early fifteenth century. It is likely that the motif originated in East Anglia.

165
Detached column surmounted by a winged figure.
83.8 x 28 cm
W.4-1916
See Architectural Museum (1877), 52, No.763a.

166
A man with a bird's head mounted on a grotesque animal.
35.6 x 17.3 cm
W.10-1916
See Architectural Museum (1877), 52, No. 757.

PLATE 60 Fragment of a stall- or bench-end from St Nicholas, King's Lynn, displaying a mantichora (cat. 163)

PLATE 61 Fragment of a bench-end from St Nicholas, King's Lynn, in the form of a semi-detached column surrounded by a winged figure (cat. 164)

167

FINIAL of a CHOIR STALL, carved in front with the arms of the town of Lynn- *three dragons' heads erect and erased, two and one, in their mouths cross-crosslets fitchy.* The shield is supported by an angel. A band of leaf ornament runs up one side, the other side is missing (PL.62).

From St Nicholas, King's Lynn

28.5 x 11.4 cm

W.11-1916

See Architectural Museum (1877), 52, No. 762. The style of this poppy-head conforms to those still remaining in the chancel in the church. The latter are among the most elaborate and sculpturally distinguished in England.The roundel scenes are lively in treatment and contain some unusual iconography.

FIG 39 Lincoln Cathedral. Stall desk-end.

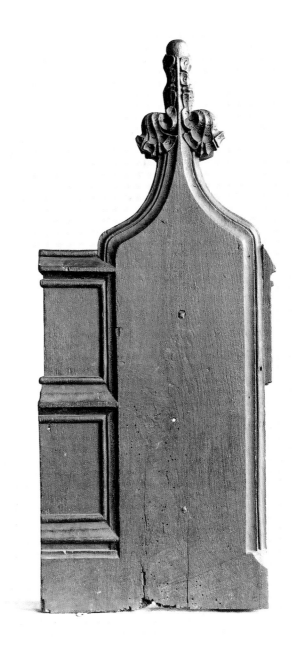

PLATE 62 Finial of a choir-stall with the arms of the town of King's Lynn (cat. 167)

PLATE 63 Bench- or stall-end from St Nicholas, King's Lynn (cat. 168)

168
BENCH- or STALL-END, with projecting side, moulded ends and top, and surmounted by a foliated poppy-head (PL.63).

109 X 53.2 X 5.08 cm

From St Nicholas, King's Lynn

W.14-1921

See Royal Architectural Museum (1877), 53, No. 793. There must have been several hands at work on the furniture at St Nicholas. The standard of carving on the poppy-heads of the three bench-ends in the same style (CAT.168-70) is run-of-the-mill by comparison with that still surviving in the choir of the church. Presumably they were a part of the congregational seating. No bench-ends like this example survive in the church any longer. It would seem that the principal purpose of the prominent moulded appendage was to allow for a greater depth of seat. The ends are otherwise undecorated.

The proportions, mouldings and carving techniques at King's Lynn are akin to some of those on the bench-ends at Wiggenhall St German's, only a few miles away. Similar plain, and decorated, stall-ends with poppy-heads and buttressed fronts can be seen on the choir-stalls as far back as Lincoln Cathedral (c.1370) (FIG.39).

169
BENCH-END, with foliated poppy-head, and
projecting elbow-rest.
From St Nicholas, King's Lynn
109 x 48.3 cm
W.2-1916
See Architectural Museum (1877), 53, No.781.

170
STALL- or BENCH-END, with foliated poppy-head, and
projecting elbow-rest.
From St Nicholas, King's Lynn
104 x 50.8 cm
Circ.36-1921

171
STALL- or BENCH-END, with moulded sides and top
surmounted by a foliated poppy-head. This is the
most common style of bench-end found at St
Nicholas. In this case the carving on the front edge
has been cut off.
From St Nicholas, King's Lynn
11 x 3.2 x 6.3 cm
W.17-1921

172
STALL- or BENCH-END, with moulded sides and top
surmounted by a foliated poppy-head carved with
pods. The carving on the front side has been cut off.
From St Nicholas, King's Lynn
97.5 x 27.9 x 5 cm
W.18-1921

173
PORTION of a STALL-END, surmounted by the figure
of a harpy, a bird with human face.
From St Nicholas, King's Lynn
61 x 6.3 x 16.5 cm
W.20-1921

174
BENCH-END, the upper part, which has lost its
poppy-head, is moulded on both sides; the end,
moulded on one side, has a projecting elbow-rest in
the form of a grotesque animal with hoofed feet
(PL.64).
From St Nicholas, King's Lynn
86.3 x 5.03 x 43.2 cm
W.56-1921

PLATE 64 Bench-end from St Nicholas, King's Lynn, with
grotesque animal with hoofed feet. Detail (cat. 174)

175
PORTION of a STALL-END, surmounted by a figure of a hoofed animal with a human head, covered with a cowl; the face missing.
From St Nicholas, King's Lynn
60.8 x 15.4 cm
W.57-1921

176
PORTION of a STALL-END, carved with a figure of a goat, the face missing.
From St Nicholas, King's Lynn
30.4 x 15.4 cm
W.58-1921

177
PORTION of a STALL-END, surmounted by a grotesque figure, the body partly missing.
From St Nicholas, King's Lynn
57.2 x 10.3 cm
W.59-1921
See Architectural Museum (1877), 52, No. 754.

178
PORTION of a STALL STANDARD, moulded in front, the elbow-rest in the form of a spotted grotesque animal with its tail in its mouth (PL.65).
From St Nicholas, King's Lynn
72.3 x 5.2 x 25.4 cm
W.60-1921
The front edge has a column attached to it with capital above. The inset quadrant shaped recess to accommodate the seat when it is being let up and down can be readily seen together with the ledge to support it.

179
POPPY-HEAD.
Probably from St Nicholas, King's Lynn.
About 1419
30.2 x 17.8 cm
Circ.26-1921

180
STALL-END, with poppy-head and figure of a griffin, with head missing, on the elbow rest.
Probably from St Nicholas, King's Lynn
About 1419
86.3 x 36.8 cm
Circ.37-1921

PLATE 65 Stall standard from St Nicholas, King's Lynn (cat. 178)

FIG 40 St George, Stowlangtoft, Suffolk. Bench-ends.

181
PART OF A STALL-END, with a carved figure of a goat.
Probably from St Nicholas, King's Lynn
About 1419
54.6 x 30 cm
Circ.38-1921

182
ELBOW-END, with carved eagle.
Probably from St Nicholas, King's Lynn
About 1419
H. 61.0 cm
Circ.41-1921

183
FRAGMENT OF STALL-END, with poppy-head.
Probably from St Nicholas, King's Lynn
About 1419
27.9 x 68.5 cm
Circ.39-1921

184-185
BENCH-ENDS, two. Each is surmounted by a poppy-head resting on an ogee moulding. One face is carved with trefoils, crocketted tracery, and finials. The elbow of each is formed by a grotesque animal or dragon, the support of which is decorated with sunk mouldings. The other face of the bench-end is cut with mortices for the seat, back and bookshelf

(PLS. 66a & b).
About 1470
112 x 49.6 x 8.2 cm
W.94 and W.95-1911
From a Suffolk church, these bench-ends correspond in style with those at Stowlangtoft (FIG.40) and Barningham in Suffolk, and must be of the same workshop.

186
UPPER PORTION of a STALL DESK-END. Beneath a crocketted ogee arch St George is raising his sword above his head about to slay the crouching dragon, the tail of which is wound round the hind legs of the horse; below is a row of shaped dentils. The upper part is shaped to form an ogee arch (PL.67).
East Anglia
15th century
52 x 26.7 x 8.6 cm
299-1907
The former owner of this piece suggested that it might have been the top of the stall of the master of the great Guild of St. George in one of the Norwich churches. The wall painting depicting the same subject at St Gregory, Norwich displays similar horse trappings (FIG.41). The general disposition of the composition and the way the dragon's tail is wound round the back leg of the horse, are also comparable.

PLATE 66 a & b Two bench-ends from a Suffolk church (cat. 184 & 185)

PLATE 67 Upper portion of a stall desk-end with carving of
St George and the Dragon (cat 186)

PLATE 68 Bench-end from Norfolk or Suffolk with human mask poppy-head (cat. 189)

FIG 41 St Gregory, Norwich. Wall painting of St George. Reproduction in watercolours by E.C. LeGrice.

187-190

BENCH ENDS, four. (1) With foliated poppy-head carved on one side, plain standard. 93.9 x 26.7 cm (2) Carved on both sides; foliated poppy-head, the lower part of standard buttressed and moulded at both ends. 107 x 38.1 cm (3) Carved on one side; the upper part of the poppy-head resembles a grotesque mask with horned head dress, the shoulders arranged as foliations; below, at one end, a buttressed and moulded elbow, originally surmounted by a figure. 104 x 40.06 cm (PL.68). (4) Carved on one side; projecting elbow buttressed and moulded on the upper part and surmounted by a seated female figure facing outwards; the poppy-head is missing (PL.69).
Given by Mr F. C. Eeles
15th century
65 x 34.6 cm
W. 74 to W. 77-1924
From a church in Norfolk or Suffolk, purchased in Bury St Edmund's, these bench-ends were thought by the donor to have come from the north of Suffolk. Plenty of examples of outward, rather than axially-facing figures placed on the buttresses of

PLATE 69 Bench-end from Norfolk or Suffolk with seated
figure on elbow buttress. Detail (cat. 190)

FIG 42 St Mary, Wilby, Suffolk. Bench-end with axially
facing figure.

FIG 43 St Nicholas, Rattlesden, Suffolk. Human mask poppy-head.

bench-ends can be cited from that area, including
Wilby (FIG.42) or Athelington. The Rattlesden, Suffolk, poppy-head is the best known example of of
foliage turning into a human mask (FIG.43). The
museum's specimen is different in that the lower
part of the carving takes the form of the mask's
body.

191
STALL- or BENCH-END with moulded top
surmounted by a foliated poppy-head.
Probably Suffolk
15th century
108 x 30.3 x 7.6 cm
W.19-1921
This is a typical symmetrical bench-end.

192
BENCH-END, carved with a poppy-head finial; one of the moulded edges is carved with a square pilaster with moulded capital and base.
Formerly in Great Wenham Church, Suffolk
15th century
117 x 40 cm
574-1898
A similar finial is illustrated in Brandon (1849), Vol. I, PL. 6. Plate 5 of the same publication shows the construction of similar seats in the church of Bentley, Suffolk.

193
POPPY-HEAD, consisting of two foliage volutes (portion of one missing) and a finial carved with a lion's mask.
Given by Mr F. C. Eeles
15th century
44.4 x 14 cm
W.418-1922
From a Norfolk or Suffolk church, similar to the Rattlesden poppy-heads although inferior in quality.

194
PORTION of a BENCH-END, the front carved with tracery and foliations. Above is a mortice for a moulded rail.
Late 15th century
76 x 29.2 cm
W.55-1921
Midland Counties (possibly North Oxfordshire), see Architectural Museum (1877), 52, No. 773. The rectangular bench-end with a straight-topped capping rail above is the characteristic form for all areas in England apart from East Anglia. Even before the days of congregational seating, the poppy-head is rarely seen on choir-stalls outside the eastern counties. Chester is an exception at the end of the fourteenth century but the choir-stalls there were made by the Lincoln workshop. The so-called 'Ripon School' of carvers (Purvis 1929 & 1935) at Ripon, Beverley Minster, Manchester Cathedral etc. used poppy-heads but, as already noted (CAT.164), it is likely that they were inspired by East Anglian precedents. At Wells Cathedral in the third decade of the fourteenth century the deskends were square headed as were contemporary stall-ends in Normandy and Brittany. Again, in the 1240s, at Salisbury Cathedral square-headed stallends are found (FIG.44). Poppy-heads sometimes

occur in the later Middle Ages in the West Country (see CAT.199).

195
BENCH-END, square-headed, with an applied moulded top, one side is carved with tracery and arcading between upright mouldings. There is a rectangular projection below, with tracery on one face. The other side is cut with mortices and holes for wooden pins to support the seat, back and bookshelf (PL.70).
From Great Tew Church, Oxfordshire
Given by Mr Aymer Vallance, F.S.A.
About 1500
81.2 x 43.2 x 11.1 cm
W.91-1911
See Parker 1850, PL.144. This is an unusual example of a square headed type of bench-end with an extension in the lower half to allow for a deeper seat.

196
BENCH-END PANEL, square-headed, in the upper part is an ogee arch with foliated cusps and with a pomegranate and foliage in the spandrels; below are grooved mouldings of linen-fold pattern; the sides are flanked by buttresses.
From a Northamptonshire church
Late 15th or early 16th century
70 x 3.1 cm
W.92-1924

197
PORTION of a BENCH-END, carved with conventional Gothic foliage in two panels. Above is a mortice for a moulded rail.
From a Devonshire church
Given by Mr A.L. Radford, F.S.A.
Late 15th or early 16th century
53.4 x 22.8 x 6.35 cm
W.199-1923

198
PORTION of a BENCH-END, carved with tracery within a crocketted ogee arch.
From a Devonshire church
Given by Mr A. L. Radford, F.S.A.
Late 15th or early 16th century
45 x 27 cm
W.200-1923

FIG 44 Salisbury Cathedral. Choir stall-end.

PLATE 70 Bench-end from
Great Tew (cat. 195)

PLATE 71 Bench-end from North Somerset (cat. 199)

199

BENCH-END, the front carved with three panels of tracery and foliage (one partly missing); the upper part which is moulded and carved at intervals with quatrefoil bosses, terminates with a lozenge-shaped finial (PL.71).
Given by Mr Mowbray A. Green, F.R.I.B.A.
15th century
109 x 30.5 cm
W.29-1923
From the West Country (probably North Somerset), these bench-ends are presumably by the same workshop as the ones at East Brent and South Brent, Somerset. See Cox 1916, 142 & 153. This is an example of a bench-end from the West Country with a poppy-head.

200

BENCH-END, square-headed, carved with tracery and two shields, one bearing the letters 'I H S' and the other a crowned 'M.'
From Linkinhorne Church, near Launceston, Cornwall
About 1500
87.5 x 31.8 cm
W.14-1910

201-202

BENCH-ENDS, two, square-headed, each carved with a panel bordered by leaf ornament, and enclosing tracery with two shields on one a hammer and unidentified image (possibly a book, or even a wrist-guard), and the other a hammer and pincers; punched decoration on the shields (PLS. 72a & b).
Devon or East Cornwall
Early 16th century
80.3 x 43.2 cm
W.17 & W.18-1913
Two of a set of fourteen bench-ends from a private museum formed early in the 19th century by the Clarkes of Bridwell, near Tiverton and sold at Christie's, Feb. 13, 1913. Stylistically these are typical of a very large class of Devonshire and Cornwall bench-ends. The motifs depicted were identified in the previous catalogue with the instruments of the Passion. However, if the unidentified image is a book, the Instruments of the Passion hypothesis would be undermined. The possibility that it is supposed to represent a wrist-guard suggests that the carver was depicting the tools of a craftsman's trade. There is a precedent for this on the stylistical-

PLATE 72 a & b Two bench-ends from Devon or East Cornwall (cat. 201 & 202)

FIG 45 St Ives Church, Cornwall. Screen fragment. Detail.

ly comparable screen fragment in St Ives Church, Cornwall depicting the implements of Ralph Clies, master-smith (FIG.45).

203-204
BENCH-ENDS, two, square-headed; the upper part of one is carved with a quatrefoil containing a shield carved with the sacred monogram, below are two semi-circular arches on twisted columns. The other has on the left a yew tree or sapin – badge of Strode, of Newnham, Devon; and on the right two rudders – badge of Willoughby de Broke, of Landulph, Cornwall; below are two semi-circular arches.
Given by Mr A. L. Radford, F.S.A.
Early 16th century
81.2 x 43 cm
W.158 & W.159-1919
Devon or East Cornwall

205
POPPY-HEAD, carved with conventional foliage.
From a Suffolk church
Given by Mr Frank Jennings
15th century
30.5 x 19.7 x 5.8 cm
W.19-1924

206
POPPY-HEAD, carved with conventional foliage, the lower part surrounded by an indented moulding.
From a Suffolk church
Given by Mr Frank Jennings
15th century
26.1 x 13.7 x 6.3 cm
W.20-1924

207
POPPY-HEAD, carved with conventional foliage, the lower part surrounded by a floral band.
From a Suffolk church.
Given by Mr Frank Jennings
15th century
26.7 x 14.6 x 6.3 cm
W.21-1924

208
PORTION of a POPPY-HEAD. The finial is in the form of a conventional flower from which springs a portion of a mutilated figure. Below on either side are half-length winged figures, of angels scaled and holding shields before them. The ogee shaped lower portion is moulded at the edges.
Given by Mr Murray Adams-Acton, through the National Art-Collections Fund
Late 15th century
48.2 x 24.2 cm
W.43-1928
Probably East Anglian.

209
TWO POPPY-HEADS, cut into two parts, with two scrolls of foliage surmounted by a finial similarly carved.
15th century
2.4 x 24.8 x 19 cm
W.28 & 28A-1926
Probably East Anglian.

210
POPPY-HEAD, decorated with leaf ornament.
15th century
35.6 x 20.3 cm, Diam. 8.2 cm
Circ.170-1914

211

POPPY-HEAD, decorated with leaf ornament.
15th century
36.2 x 22.2 cm, Diam. 6.7 cm
Circ.172-1914

212

POPPY-HEAD, decorated with leaf ornament.
15th century
34.8 x 22.2 cm, Diam. 7 cm
Circ.174-1914

213

POPPY-HEAD, decorated with leaf ornament.
15th century
43.5 x 22.2 cm
218-1897

214

STALL-END, with poppy-head finial; the outer side
moulded with projecting buttress and moulded
base.
Late 15th century
123 x 40.7 cm
W.39-1934
East Anglian, alleged to have come from Norwich
Cathedral, although this attribution is doubtful.

215-217

BENCH-END, FRONT PORTION OF A BENCH-END and
FRAGMENT OF ANOTHER BENCH-END; the complete
bench-end with paired arm-rests, on the outer face,
at the top, affronted crouching hounds head
downwards, lying on an ogee arch, and below
three tiers of blind arcading in countersunk relief
(PLS. 73a,b & c).
Given by Mr A.D. Passmore
Late 15th or early 16th century
Portion of bench-end (121 x 160 cm), Front portion
of a bench-end (91.3 x 34.3 cm), Complete bench-
end with paired arm rests (104 x 45.7 cm).
W.8, 9 & 10-1958
These fragments were stated by the donor to have
come from Balderton, Notts. They are identical in
type and general design with the bench-ends at St
Giles' Church (FIG.46). The Balderton bench-ends are
either surmounted by affronted hounds or hares.
The bench-ends at the nearby church of Holme
have similar simple hollow mouldings but are completely undecorated except for foliage poppy-
heads. They do, however, feature affronted animals
and human figures on the mouldings on either side
of the poppy-heads. These are reminiscent of the

PLATE 73 a, b & c Portions of bench-ends from Balderton,
Notts (cat. 215-217)

FIG 46 St Giles, Balderton, Nottinghamshire. Bench-end.

animals at Balderton, although they are not down-wards facing. Holme church was enlarged and refur-nished by John Barton in about 1485 (he died in 1491). The Balderton and Holme furniture may well be by the same workshop, the former probably being the later of the two. The juxtaposition of the two is intriguing. The Holme bench-ends lack the rather mechanical elaboration of the sunk tracery at Balderton but the sculpture itself is far more varied. The monotonous repetition of the same motifs at Balderton accords with the stereotyped presentation of the bench-end decoration. This perhaps suggests that the patron at Holme took a greater personal interest in his commission and was not primarily concerned to get the work done in a hurry.

FIG 47 Westminster Abbey. Figure of Virgin from Annunciation group on Henry V chantry.

218
POPPY-HEAD, decorated with foliage ornament.
15th century
25.4 x 19 x 8.2 cm
668-1902

219
POPPY-HEAD, decorated with foliage ornament.
15th century
35.2 x 17.3 cm
669A-1902

220
POPPY-HEAD, decorated with leaf ornament.
15th century
35.2 x 17.3 cm
670-1902

221-232
TWELVE POPPY-HEADS, with foliage ornament.
33.6 cm to 36.2 x 19.7 cm to 22.2 cm
15th century
W.76 to K-1914

233
PORTION OF STALL-END, made from a single plank of oak; in the centre an arch with cusping in the head and quatrefoils in the spandrels.
From North Cheriton Church, Somerset
15th century
81.2 x 45 x 3.2 cm
W.53-1931

PORTION OF CUPBOARD

234-235
TWO DOORS from a CUPBOARD, carved in high relief, one with the Virgin and Child standing beneath a round arch, the other with St John the Evangelist holding a chalice in his left hand. There are marks on each of a foliated lock plate and hinge bands (PL.74a & b).
Mid 15th century
38.1 x 25.7 cm
W.5 & W.6-1911
The broken, jagged and angular drapery with stiff voluminous folds is similar to the drawing style on the museum's corbel (CAT.45) probably of the mid fifteenth century. This style was introduced in the Netherlands about 1430 and it is seen on the Annunciation figures of the Henry V chantry at Westminster Abbey of the 1440s (FIGS. 8 & 47). The way of arranging the hair in rolls on the figure of St John can be seen on Gabriel at Westminster Abbey and, again, on the museum's corbel.

PLATE 74 a & b Two doors from a cupboard with carved
figures of the Virgin and St John the Evangelist (cat. 234 & 235)

122 *Portion of Cupboard*

236

FINIAL, from a font-cover; the upper part carved
with foliage, the lower part moulded; surmounted
by an iron ring. It has traces of the original gold and
colour. There the fragments of mouldings
converging at the top (PL.75).
Probably East Anglian
About 1340
91.2 x 16.5 cm
W.27-1921

Font covers are usually either flat or cone-shaped.
In the latter case the body of the cover can be
either skeletal or panelled *e.g.* Wheathampstead,
Herts (FIG.48). The museum's finial comes from a
conical cover. The number of mouldings converging at the top indicates that the cover was octagonal. The foliage used is the voluted 'trefoil' leaf found
on the choir-stalls at Ely (*c.*1340) and elsewhere at
that time (*e.g.*the John of Eltham tomb at Westminster Abbey, and the King's Lynn cup). This leaf
was also much used in the fifteenth century also but
the robustness of this carving speaks of the fourteenth century.

FIG 48 St Helen, Wheathampstead, Hertfordshire.
Font cover.

PLATE 75 Finial of font cover (cat. 236)

PORTIONS OF A SHRINE

237

NINETEEN SMALL PANELS, pierced with tracery probably from a shrine.
The dimensions vary from H. 14.6 to 21.6 cm, from W. 3.8 to 7.6 cm
15th century
221 to 221R-1897

238

THREE UPPER PORTIONS OF PANELS, each decorated with an applied ogee-shaped arch (modern) enriched with crockets and a finial; the rest of each panel is pierced with tracery. Each probably formed part of a shrine. There are traces of gilding.
The height of each is just less than 25.4 cm in and the width 10-15 cm
15th century
150, 150A & 150B-1897

It is reasonable to assume that all the fragments in this section came from the same shrine as they were acquired at the same time. Given the fragmentary nature of the museum's specimens, it is impossible to make any meaningful comparisons. The only surviving English wooden shrine is possibly the cupboard in Wensley Church, N. Yorkshire, to which an alms box is attached (FIG.49). (See Howard & Crossley 1917, 342). This is said to have come from Easby Abbey.

FIG 49 Holy Trinity, Wensley, N. Yorkshire. Possible wooden shrine and alms box.

COLOUR PLATES

PLATE 1 St Katherine's Hospital-by-the-Tower. View of choir from the east. Watercolour drawing by John Carter. 1780 (Port of London Authority Collection – Museum of London).

ST. CATHERINES

5.76

View inside of St.
Catherines which
near the Tower taken
1780 Drawn large
for Dr Ducarell

ORIGINAL DRAWING BY JOHN CARTER SKETCHED FOR
Dr DUCAREL 1780

PLATE 2 Boss from St Alban's Abbey with lion gnawing a bone
W.51-1914 (cat. 17).

PLATE 3 Four panels from a reredos
W.34 to W.34c-1912 (cat. 62-65).

PLATE 4 Parclose screen panel from Great Barton, Suffolk with painted Annunciation W.50-1921 (cat. 94).

PLATE 5 Panel from St John Maddermarket, Norwich with St Agatha and St William of Norwich 24-1894 (cat. 101).

PLATE 6 Panels from St John Maddermarket, Norwich with St Leonard and St Agnes
23-1894 (cat. 100).

PLATE 7 Four panels from a rood screen with Adoration of the Magi, West Country
W.54-1928 (cat. 102).

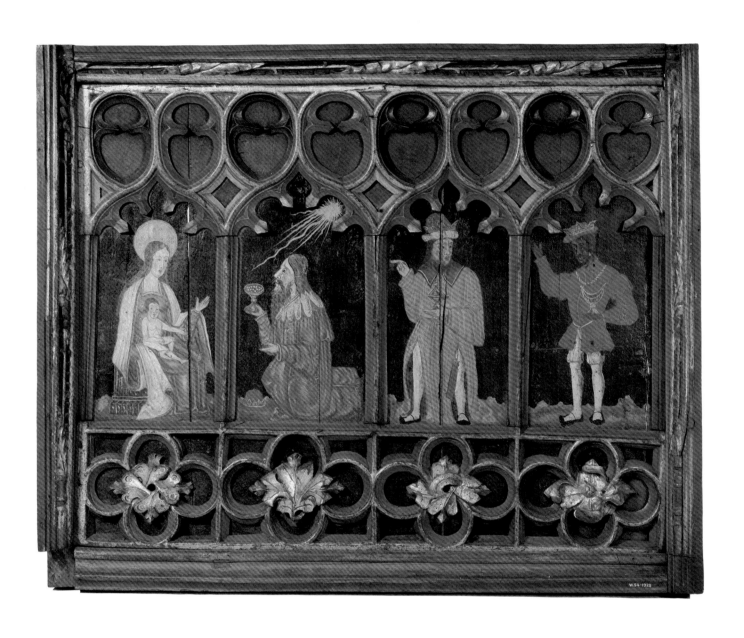

DOMESTIC

PLATE 76 Corner-post, known
as 'Finney's Post' (cat. 239)

DOMESTIC

A. STRUCTURAL WOODWORK AND FITTINGS

CORNER-POSTS

239

CORNER or JETTY-POST, known as 'Finney's Post'; the lower part has on each of the two faces a pair of arched panels, the lower two containing a portcullis; in the middle of the post is a raised band surmounted by battlementing and having two projecting turrets at the corners; the upper part is formed of three curved spurs, the face of each carved with traceried arches (PL.76).
Probably first half of 15th century
222 x 58.5 cm square
W.42-1920

The post belonged to a building in the market-place at Burton-on-Trent, called the Garrets, formerly used as a residence for the canons of the collegiate church. On the destruction of the building it was moved to Plas-Newydd in the Isle of Anglesey, and at the sale there about 1850 it was bought by Mr Robert Thornewill, of Burton Abbey, whose son moved it to Craythorne, near Burton. It was afterwards lent to the Museum at Burton-on-Trent. The post was called 'Finney's Post,' after a merchant of Burton by name of Finney. It is related that Finney's wife, who had the reputation for being a scold, fell into a trance; and while her bier was being borne to the graveyard it hit against the post. She thereupon recovered consciousness and lived, it is stated, for several years afterwards, much to the disappointment of her husband. In the early part of the 19th-century a brass plate was fixed to the post, engraved with the following lines:-

> "This Post, as Finney's Legend saith,
> Awoke a Scolding Wife from Death;
> But when at length she ceas'd to breathe,
> And honest Finney ceased to grieve,
> 'oh shun' he said, as borne along,
> With solemn dirge and funeral song,
> 'Oh shun, my friends, that cruel Stump
> That gave my dear so hard a Bump."
>
> J.S.

240

CORBEL-BRACKET or CORNER-POST of a half-timbered house, carved with a full-length bowed figure of a wild man or 'woodwose' with hairy body and wearing high boots and holding a knotted club in his hands, who stands against a background of conventional foliage, his feet on a monster's mask, his head supporting a moulded capital (One foot of the figure and the monster's tongue have been restored). (PL.77).
Given by Mr Frank Surgey, through the National Art-Collections Fund
About 1500
127 x 21.9 x 36.8 cm
W. 6-1928

In contemporary pageantry the 'woodwose' was often represented, and the London Chronicles for 1505 describe a procession in which 'came... the Erle of Essex w^t a woodhous precedyng and beryng a sere tre.' John Carter illustrates a woodwose corner-post 'against a house at the place where East gate stood (the house being without the gate)' at Bury St Edmund's. It was fully life-size in height (nearly two metres). See Carter (1780).

241-242

CORNER-POSTS, two. One of the posts has a projecting canopy in the form of two arches outlined by interlacing foliage; beneath the canopy are two shields, one on each face, bearing the arms of Heigham and Cotton, and Heigham and Calthorp; the rest of the surface below the shields is covered with conventional scrolling foliage. The other post has, below the projecting canopy, the arms of Heigham and Calthorp and Poley, and the arms of Heigham alone; the rest of the surface is decorated with tracery (PL.78a & b).
From a house, now destroyed, in Bury St. Edmund's
Second quarter of 16th century
157 x 3.80 cm
W.6 and W.7-1909

The arms on the first post are those of Catherine Cotton, wife of Thomas Heigham, of Heigham, Cambs., d. 1492; and (2) of Elizabeth Calthorp, d. 1542, first wife of Thomas Heigham, of Bury St Edmund's, their grandson. Those on the other post are (1) of Thomas Heigham, of Bury St Edmund's, combined with those of his two wives, Calthorp and Poley; and (2) of Thomas Heigham, of Bury St

Edmund's, alone. The arms date from the period of the marriage of Thomas Heigham, of Bury St Edmund's, with a lady of the family of Poley, on the death of his first wife, Elizabeth Calthorp, in 1542. The date of the Poley alliance is unknown. See Hervey 1871, 230. In 1871 these posts were in the possession of C. W. Heigham, of Wetherden. See also Corder (1918), 8 & PL.8.

It has been pointed out that from these posts it is possible to estimate the approximate height of the rooms for which they were made (Cescinsky and Gribble 1922, I, 49-50). Allowing for a brick plinth of about 61 cm with the deduction of about 15 cm for a step from ground to floor level, the height of the room from the floor to the underside of the joists must have been less that 21 m. The decoration of these posts well exemplifies the unselfconscious coexistence at this time of the Gothic and Renaissance styles.

243
BEAM or CORNICE, from the front of a house, the angle of the face bevelled off and decorated with five quatrefoil bosses.
Given by Mr T. Charbonnier
15th century
16.5 x 17.8 cm
A.14-1909
West Country

244
CORNICE or FRIEZE, from the front of a house, carved in high relief with scrolling branches of vine with leaves.
From an old house in Honiton, Devon
Early 16th century
14.6 x 274 x 9 cm
W. 66-1911.

PLATE 77 Corbel-bracket or corner-post with figure of woodwose (cat. 240)

PLATE 78 a & b Two corner-posts from Bury St Edmund's with heraldic decoration (cat. 241 & 242)

245
WINDOW-FRAME, consisting of a framework of
heavy beams enclosing five lights divided by
mullions moulded on front and back; the top of
each light is occupied by an ogee arch with
openwork tracery (PL.79).
From a house in Hadleigh, Suffolk
Given by Mr A. H. Fass
Late 15th century
18 x 22 cm
W.59-1913
This window must have always been intended to
be unglazed. The tracery on both sides is carved and
the mullions moulded. On the inside face there are
still traces of decorated plaster-work. The rebates
on the interior faces must have been for shutters. It
has been pointed out (Cescinsky and Gribble 1922,
52-53) that these window-frames again demonstrate
(compare the Bury St Edmund's corner-posts,
CATS.241-42) that ceilinged rooms at this time must
have been very low even in timber houses of the
more elaborate kind. The height of this excep-
tionally fine window is less than 1.8 m. Even allowing for the cutting of the lower parts of the uprights, where they rested on the wall-plate, the
total height of the room cannot have been more
than 2.1 m. Fifteenth-century doors made for secular timber-framed houses are rarely over 1.8 m. in
height.

246
HEAD of a WINDOW, consisting of two trefoil-
headed lights; in the centre of each light is a hole for
an iron bar.
From a house in Lustleigh, Devon
Given by Mr Mark Nickols
15th century
about 19.0 x 119 cm
A.86-1918

PLATE 79 Window-frame from a house in Hadleigh, Essex (cat. 245)

247

ARCH or CARTWAY, pointed and depressed; in the left spandrel is a boy holding by the tongue a dolphin terminating in scrolling leaves; in the right is a similar dolphin with a fish biting its tail. Above is a projecting cornice supported on two brackets. The jambs are moulded (PL.80).
From the Church Farm, Clare, Suffolk
Early 16th century
726-1902
Compare the archway at Paycocke's House, Coggeshall, Essex (FIG.50).

248

DOORWAY and DOOR; the doorway has a depressed pointed arch with a boss and a long serrated leaf in each spandrel; the lintel and jambs are moulded. The square-headed door consists of six slightly moulded vertical planks overlapping one another and studded with four rows of twelve iron nails, two of which are arranged on each plank. There are two hinges with long bands on the back and the marks of two long hinge bands on the front; it is also fitted with a latch and bolt of wrought iron (PL.80).
From the Church Farm, Clare, Suffolk
Early 16th century
254 x 1.29 cm
727-1902
Described in Oliver 1912, FIG.22 as 'A thoroughly East Anglian example, typical of hundreds which formerly existed in all three counties'. The mixture of styles used in the decoration is noticeable. In the door-head spandrels the leaf motif is typical of the fifteenth century, as are also the buttresses on either side of the cartway (CAT.NO.247). Yet the spandrel carving of the cartway head is pure Renaissance in design.

249

DOORWAY and DOOR. The jambs are moulded and have superimposed small circular columns with moulded capitals and bases and are surmounted by carved brackets. The lintel is moulded and carved with dentils. The doorway has a depressed arch with narrow spandrels filled with conventional foliage. The door is strengthened by moulded mullions and carved with a simple linenfold pattern; the smaller door, or wicket, has an ogee-shaped head (PL.81).
From a house formerly in Key Street, Ipswich

FIG 50 Paycocke's House, Coggeshall, Essex. Archway and door

Given by Sir George Donaldson
Early 16th century
305 x 194 cm
A.25-1913

250

UPPER PORTION of a DOORWAY; a depressed pointed arch, in each spandrel of which is a leaf with serrated edges and a circular boss in the centre.
Early 16th century
28.5 x 117 cm
1968-1900
Said to have come from Sutton Place, near Guildford, Surrey.

PLATE 80 Arch or cartway, and doorway and door from
the Church Farm, Clare, Suffolk (cat. 247 & 248)

PLATE 81 Doorway and door
from Key Street, Ipswich
(cat. 249)

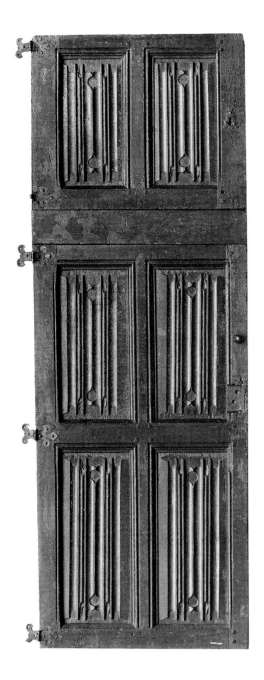

PLATE 82 Linenfold door in two parts (cat. 251)   PLATE 83 Linenfold door from Lavenham, Suffolk (cat. 252)

251
DOOR, in two parts; one consisting of four and the
other of two linenfold panels; one has an oak
handle, and the other an iron escutcheon, and both
are fitted with hinges of tinned iron (PL.82).
Given by Mr Murray Marks
Early 16th century
134 cm and 51 x 66 cm
W.68-1916
Stated to have come from South Wales.

252
DOOR, composed of four panels of linenfold
ornament, in a moulded framework (PL.83).
From Lavenham, Suffolk
Early 16th century
175 x 67.5 cm
W.57-1913
It has been suggested that the 'linenfold' device
may have been copied from the curling of parchment, which was sometimes glued to the backs of
painted panels to stiffen them and to help prevent
them from cracking. Parchment would not stick

easily to an oak panel and might tend to curl up at the edges. Cescinsky suggested that the use of the vertical ridge, which is such a prominent feature of the 'linenfold' design, may have originated in the chamfering on the backs of early panels, each plane tending to meet in a low ridge in the middle (Cescinsky and Gribble 1922, I, 245). The simple chamfered ornament (FIG.51) was very commonly employed. These hypotheses seem unnecessarily far-fetched when the practice of breaking up the surface of a door with vertical mouldings, using lamination or clinker-boarding, and battening techniques, had already been used for a very long time. They also have a familiar utilitarian ring to them. Nor was the development of this kind of decoration dependant upon the use of true panel and frame construction. Indeed the stubborn survival of the idea of using textiles, in the form of wicker-work or drapery, as room partitions was first discussed by Gottfried Semper (see Michael Podro, *The Critical Historians of Art*, New Haven and London, 1982, 46-47 & Chapter IV, n.7). Textiles, used so much in the Middle Ages as interior furnishings of one kind or another, are more likely to have provided the inspiration for linenfold ornament (Eames 1977, 274-76).

A somewhat tentative form of linenfold decoration can be seen in the fifteenth-century lap-jointed wainscotting in such places as the porch of the Guildhall at Lavenham. This is effectively unframed and secured to the wall with nails. Cescinsky insisted that where vertical mouldings are flat, and the decoration is confined to the ends of the panels, it is incorrect to talk of 'linenfold'. The museum's door, on the other hand, he classifies as true linenfold since the mouldings represent rolled-up linen. Sometimes the rods around which the fabric was rolled are also incorporated in the design. The ribbing was produced by means of specially-made moulding planes and the decorative carving at top and bottom was done by hand.

The earliest datable example of true linenfold in England, so far identified are the doors of the Audley Chapel at Hereford Cathedral (Eames 1977, 275). referred to in the accounts of 1492 as *lignum undulatum*. It is unlikely that the motif appeared in England much later than on the Continent, although all the surviving examples here must be of the sixteenth century

The plastic treatment of the linenfold 'hems' on this door approach the character of late Gothic 'banderole' on the Continent.

FIG 51 Luton Museum (Bagshawe Collection). Panel with simple chamfered ornament.

253
DOOR, composed of eight panels of linenfold ornament, in a moulded framework (PL.84).
Early 16th century
174 x 61 cm
368-1905
Stated to have come from Norwich. Although the ribbing on this door is rather flat the roll of fabric is clearly identifiable with a decorated border top and bottom. The rails are butted square into the stiles as in the previous door, and the mouldings turned and mitred to meet those on the vertical muntins on stonemasonry principles.

PLATE 84 Linenfold door
probably from Norwich
(cat. 253)

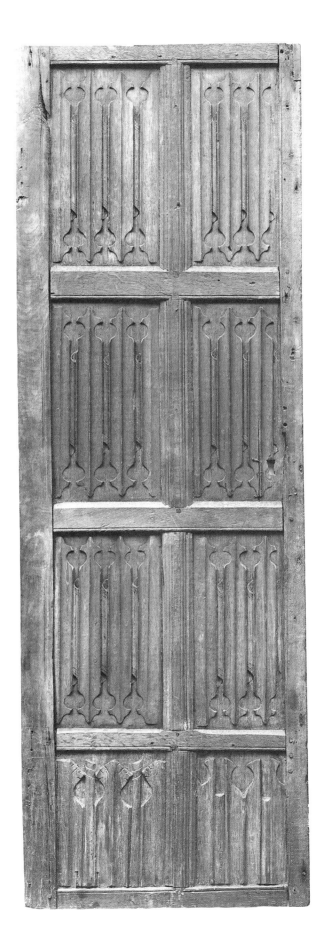

Square-headed, panelled DOOR, decorated with
two rows of applied arcading, fastened by
decorative iron nails, the heads of the arches being
filled with plate pierced tracery. The spandrels are
filled with rosettes and leaf ornament, except the
central one in the top row, in which are two
interlacing triangles. Under the upper arcade is a
band of small panels, one of which contains a
recumbent figure, one a dragon and the six others
animals; under the lower arcade are five
compartments, the central one containing floral
ornament and the two on either side enclosing a
fish and a bird respectively. The door has been
restored and the ornament on the lower part of it is
missing. The back was secured by a series of six flat
iron straps with flanged ends. Two of these must
have been used to carry the door hinges but these
are now missing.

The left-hand spandrel of the central tier is left
uncarved and the centre one is missing its original
sculpture which was probably a mask, the ears of
which survive on either side. The central spandrel
carving of the lower tier arcading was probably
decorated with another mask. Approximately 46
cm of door has been cut off at the bottom. Some of
the scribing lines of the design of this section are
visible and it is clear that another identical register
existed. This would have brought the total height
of the door to some 2.7 m. The lower part of the
front side of the door is very weathered.

Presumably, for this reason, when it was
purchased by the museum in 1895, it was suggested
that it had been an outside door. Such an elaborate
and secure structure, the existence of a key-hole on
the left-hand side and the scars of hinge straps,
argue that this must have been a door rather than
the section of a screen (PL.85).

From the Peyre Collection

About 1300

228 x 126 cm

754-1895

The style of architecture employed is a mixture of
bar in the uprights and plate tracery in the arcading.
The composition of doubled sub- within acute two-
centred arches is reminiscent of Rayonnant buildings in England like Westminster Abbey. But the
retention of plate tracery elements gives the composition an old-fashioned look. A similar comprom-
ise was reached in the mid thirteenth-century rood-
screen at Stanton Harcourt, Oxon (FIG.52). In both
cases the technique of carving the arcade out of a
single thick wide plank of wood was employed. In

FIG 52 St Michael, Stanton Harcourt, Oxon. Rood screen.
Detail.

this context, of course, the use of free-standing or
applied columns flouts Victorian principles of
structural honesty.

The foliage is naturalistic in type but rather sche-
matically treated, although in the central tier there
are some delicately serrated rose leaves. The
mythical figures include a dragon with human head
of the type seen on the misericords at Exeter
Cathedral (before 1244). Such motifs crop up con-
tinually in medieval art. The interlocking triangle
device in the central spandrel is the basis of the
'prism' type of chip-carved design to be seen in
English chests of the thirteenth century (See
CAT.206).

The door can be usefully compared to the framing of the Thornham Parva retable (FIG.53). The

PLATE 85 Square-headed
arcaded door (cat. 254)

FIG 53 St Mary, Thornham Parva, Suffolk. Retable. Detail.

latter, although it lacks the subdivided arches, uses the same attached colonnettes with, essentially, bar tracery above. The method of carving the tracery-heads from a single plank of wood, in two sections in this case, was quite out of fashion in progressive joinery circles by the early fourteenth century when the wooden framing of the Suffolk monument must have been constructed.

The square-headed profile of this door may indicate a secular application. Moreover, the door does not seem to have been protected by a porch. Given its considerable height when intact it is more likely to have been associated with a stone rather than a timber-framed building. Clearly this must have been a structure of some pretension.

255

CEILING, composed of four wall beams, a cross-beam, thirty-six rafters and thirty-eight boards. The lower inner edge of each wall beam is chamfered and moulded; in two of them the socket, into which the cross-beam fits, is decorated with leafwork. The cross-beam and rafters have chamfered and moulded lower edges, and the cross-beam is further decorated on the under surface with leafwork twined round a rod; the chamfers on the rafters are stopped with leaves.
From the Church Farm, Clare, Suffolk
Late 15th or early 16th century
67 x 626 cm
725-1902
The panelling of this room, purchased by Sir Charles Lawes-Wittewronge, is now at Rothamsted Park, Herts (B.O.E., *Hertfordshire*, 159).

256

BEAM, from a ceiling. Slightly pediment-shaped; in the centre is a plain shield on either side of which is a long serrated leaf twisted round a rod; above and below are plain mouldings.
Said to have come from Sutton Place, near Guildford
Early 16th century
33 x 325 x 24.7 cm
1966-1900
Sutton Place was built about 1525 by Sir Richard Weston, ambassador from Henry Henry VIII to Francis I. See Harrison (1893), and Dell (1905).

257

BEAM (fragment), from a ceiling, of chestnut, the face carved with conventional foliage and diagonal bands over a central rod; the moulded sides 'stopped' with leaf ornament.
Given by Mrs. C. Phillips
15th century
118 x 17.8 x 8.9 cm
W.69-1924
The building from which this beam comes was formerly part of St John's Hospital, Duxford, Cambs, the former chapel of which still stands beside it.

258

BOSS, of oak from the ceiling of a house, carved with cusps and two crockets in the form of conventional leaves.
Purchased from the Frank Jennings Collection

15th century
16 x 31.5 cm
W.13-1924
Said to have come from Suffolk.

259

BEAM, probably from a roof. A depressed pointed arch, in each spandrel a leaf with serrated edges, and a circular depression in the centre.
Said to have come from Sutton Place, near Guildford
Early 16th century
43.2 x 137 cm
1967-1900

260

PORTIONS of BEAMS, eleven, from ceilings or screens, carved with conventional foliage (PL.86).
About 1500
Various sizes, from 68.5 cm to 127 cm
W.28 to W.37 and W.62-1921
Probably from Suffolk or Essex. Formerly in the Royal Architectural Museum, Westminster.

261

CHIMNEY-BEAM; the front is divided by two intersecting diagonal lines into four triangular compartments, the two at the sides being each filled with a long serrated leaf and a rosette. The upper and lower compartments are blank. Below is a convex moulding.
From a house near Exeter
First half of 16th century
24.8 x 185 x 13.3 cm
587-1901
The correct name for the lintel or mantel over a fireplace is 'clavel.' The term 'breast-sumner,' 'bressomer' or 'bressumer' (the 'sumner' or beam over a large opening) is sometimes times inaccurately employed for the chimney-beam or 'clavel.'

262

PORTIONS of a CORNICE or CRESTING. The ornament consists of the repetition of leaf forms, partly carved in openwork, springing from a series of alternate large and small cusps; below is a moulding (PL.87).
Said to have come from Sutton Place, near Guildford
Early 16th century
19 x about 61 cm
1969 to 1969F-1900

PLATE 86 Portions of beams from Suffolk or Norfolk (cat. 260)

PLATE 87 Piece of cornice or cresting from Sutton Place, Guildford (cat. 262)

263
CORNICE, carved with a vine branch.
52 x 14 x 7.6 cm
Early 16th century
Circ. 296-1911

264
PORTION of a BEAM, carved with grapes and leaves
About 1500
68.5 x 17.8 x 12.7 cm
W.63-1921

265
PORTION of a BEAM.
Early 16th century
12 x 108 cm
Circ.93-1921.

266

SCREEN, with decoration in carved relief and painted colours consisting of three portions, which before restoration were separate, consisting of three Perpendicular bays between carved jambs; linenfold and parchment ornament in three rows, in the centre portion, between similar tracery and three similar rows of decoration, are three shields of arms, one in each bay, the tinctures painted in colours (PL.88).

183 x 335 cm

About 1500

W.1-1946

From the Old Manor House, Brightleigh, North Devon, formerly in the possession of a branch of the family of Giffard. The heraldry representing Giffard alliances is not yet certainly identified. The screen was drastically restored before 1919 by Harry Hems, of Exeter. This is a rare instance of a late medieval screen of domestic origin.

Cescinsky (1922, I, 235) illustrates it before restoration and gives a conjectural reconstruction of the entire structure as it would have been originally. There were two openings to give access to the screens passage and, quite possibly, a loft above. An early photograph betrays the fact that the left-hand panel of the right section has been fitted back to front. The left-hand section at that time still retained the base of the springing of the door arch. Also the scar of the original dado is visible at the bottom of each panel.

PLATE 88 Hall screen from Brightleigh, Devon. Detail (cat. 266)

PLATE 89 Panel fragment with Royal Arms of England (cat. 268)

267

PANELLING of a room (incomplete), carved with linenfold ornament set in vertical stiles moulded and chamfered, and plain horizontal rails with scratch mouldings.

From a farmhouse near Monmouth

First half 16th century

Total length about 913 cm, average height about 259 cm

W. 35-1913

268

PANEL; the remaining half of a large panel of the Royal Arms of England. Below is carved a figure of an heraldic lion, rampant guardant, as one of the supporters; above is a section of an ogee arch with foliated crockets, the spandrel of which has, in one niche a full-length figure in armour and in another a half-length figure holding a shield. In the background below the arch is a trail of roses and the outlines of three shields, which probably contained painted coats-of-arms. The arch is supported by pilasters, one of which is decorated with a chevron moulding. From Lower Docker Hall, Lancashire (V.C.H., *Lancashire*, VIII, 1914, 246. (PL.89).

Given by Murray Adams-Acton, Esq., through the National Art-Collections Fund

165 x 32.5 cm

About 1480

W.2-1928

Roe (1928a) suggested that this fragment may have formed part of a back panel or 'dossal' of a seat of state in a medieval hall.

269

SHIELD OF ARMS, carved with the Royal Arms of England, as borne by the Plantagenet kings, supported on either side by a winged angel flying horizontally and wearing a long flowing robe (PL.90).

Early 16th century

25.4 x 1.25 cm

W.34-1927

This is sculpture of high quality, and in view of the eccentricity of the heraldry (the lions passant guardant are facing in the wrong direction), could just as easily be French as English. However the bulky angular folds of the drapery can be matched on the angels in the early sixteenth-century tomb of Sir Edmund Gorges at Wraxall, Avon (FIG.54). The rhythmic swinging S-curve of the figures is echoed in the slightly less accomplished but stylistically re-

PLATE 90 Royal Arms of England supported by winged angels (cat. 269)

FIG 54 All Saints, Wraxall, Avon. Tomb of Sir Edmund Gorges. Detail.

lated figures on the tomb of Sir Richard Knightley (d.1534) at Fawsley, Northants.

270
PANELLING, composed of ten panels, carved with linenfold in a moulded framework; above is a cresting carved with lozenges, circles and floral devices, and divided into lengths by uprights with carved finials (PL.91).
Early 16th century
104 x 1.9 cm
539-1892
From a farmhouse, now destroyed, at Kingston, near Taunton, Somerset. Figured in Roe 1902, 116 and Robinson 1905, PL.XIII. This panelling may originally have formed the back of a fixed settle like the one, about 1500, in the abbot's parlour at Muchelney, Somerset.

271
PANELLING, composed of five panels of linenfold ornament within a moulded framework (PL.92).
First half of 16th century
77 cm x 236 cm
661-1904

272
PANEL, carved with linenfold pattern.
Early 16th century
57 x 27 cm
Given by the Architectural Association
W.21-1916
Formerly in the Royal Architectural Museum, Westminster.

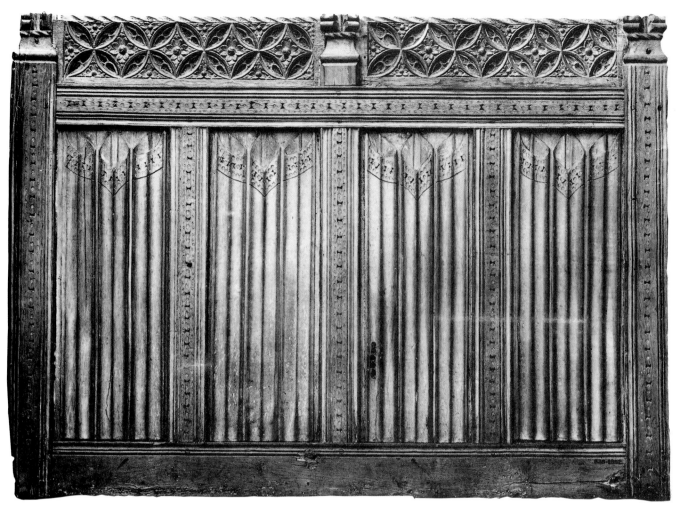

PLATE 91 Linenfold panelling possibly from the back of a settle (cat. 270)

PLATE 92 Five panels of linenfold ornament (cat. 271)

PLATE 94 Linenfold panel with spiral ends (cat. 276)

273
PANEL, carved with linenfold pattern and rosettes.
Given Mr Sydney Vacher
53.3 x 20.3 cm
About 1500
W. 38-1918
Formerly in the Royal Architectural Museum, Westminster.

274
PANEL, carved with linenfold pattern, the central fold terminating in volutes.
Late 15th or early 16th century
39.4 x 22.2 cm
W.64-1921
Formerly in the Royal Architectural Museum, Westminster.

275
PANEL, carved with linenfold pattern, the central fold terminating in volutes with a fold on either side terminating in conventional spirals.
Late 15th or early 16th century
47 x 25.4 cm
W.65-1921
Formerly in the Royal Architectural Museum, Westminster.

276
PANEL, carved with linenfold pattern, three of the folds terminating in volutes, and between them two folds with spiral ends. Stamped foliate decoration (PL.94).
Early 16th century
45.7 x 21.6 cm
W.42-1921
Formerly in the Royal Architectural Museum, Westminster.

277
PANEL, carved with linenfold arranged in two tiers (PL.93).
About 1500
28.4 x 17.8 cm
W.8-1930
Given by Mr Aymer Vallance
The panel was bought at Oxford in 1884. The treatment of the linen folds closely resembles that of the panelling in the Hall of Magdalen College.

278
PANEL, carved in relief with two curved ribs set back to back, with a rose and leaves above and

PLATE 93 Linenfold panel
(cat. 277)

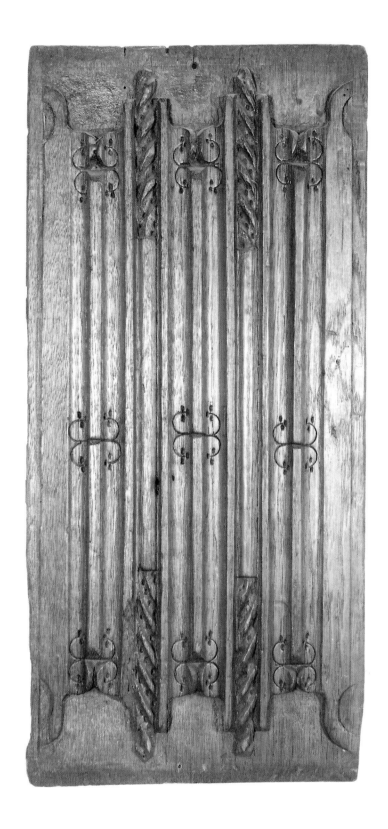

PLATE 95 Parchemin panel with rose, vine, thistle and hop foliage (cat. 278)

PLATE 96 Parchemin panel with grapes and leaves (cat. 279)

below, and tendrils with grapes, thistle, rose, and hops on either side (PL.95).
Late 15th or early 16th century
55.8 x 27.3 cm
W.66-1921
Formerly in the Royal Architectural Museum, Westminster. This decoration is usually called 'parchemin' (see CATS.279 & 313). Its origins seem to be different from linenfold. They probably go back to the parchment scrolls held by prophets and others in the manuscripts and wall paintings of the earlier Middle Ages.

279
PANEL, carved in relief with two curved ribs set back to back and a conventional design of grapes and leaves (PL.96).
Given by Mr A. Fass

Late 15th or early 16th century
63.5 x 2 cm
W.153-1921
Purchased by the donor in Suffolk.

280
PORTION of a PANEL, carved and painted light brown. The decoration consists of bunches of grapes, cusping, conventional foliage and portion of a shield with the device of a bird rising.
Norfolk.
Given by Fred Roe, Esq., R.I.
About 1500
35.6 x 18.4 cm
W.40-1928
From the collection of Canon R. Gordon Roe, formerly Rector of Acle, Norfolk.

PLATE 97 Linenfold panel with oak leaves and pine cones (cat. 281)

281
PANEL, carved with linenfold pattern; the folds
terminate in a conventional pattern of oak leaves,
and on one side is an ornament representing a pine
cone (PL.97).
Suffolk or Essex
Given by Mr Fred Roe, R.I.
Early 16th century
40.7 x 33 cm
W.39-1928
Found by the donor in an old house at Colchester.

282-283
PANELS, two, carved with two curved ribs set back
to back, decorated at the top and bottom with
foliated cusps. Within the curves at the sides are the
initials 'G' and 'L' in Gothic and Tudor characters
(PL.98).
Early 16th century
33 x 33 cm
W.48 and W.48A-1914

PLATE 98 Parchemin panel with foliated cusps and initials
'G' and 'T' (cat. 282)

PLATE 99 Parchemin panel with Lombardic initials 'M' and 'T' (cat. 284)

284
PANEL, carved in relief with two curved ribs set
back to back;, within the curves on the top and
bottom are trailing vines, and on each side similar
ornaments and the initial 'M,' in Lombardic
character on one side and Tudor on the other
(PL.99).
Early 16th century
48.3 x 28 cm
W.49-1914

285
PORTION of a PANEL, with linenfold ornament.
15th century
43.3 x 19.4 cm
488-1898

PLATE 100 Flamboyant panels
from Sutton Place, Guildford
(cat. 286)

PLATE 101 Linenfold panel with leaves and fruit (cat. 294)

286
TWO PORTIONS of PANELLING, carved in openwork with three panels of flamboyant tracery carved on both sides, the framework moulded (PL.100).
From Sutton Place, Guildford
Early 16th century
198 x 48.3 cm (1974), 50.8 cm (1974a).
1974 & 1974A-1900
Possibly Continental.

287
PORTION of linenfold PANELLING.
15th century
50.8 x 22.8 cm
Circ.44-1921

288
PORTION of linenfold PANELLING.
15th century
52.1 x 20.3 cm
Circ.48-1921

289
PORTION of linenfold PANELLING.
15th century
57.2 x 25.4 cm
Circ.49-1921

290
PORTION of linenfold PANELLING.
15th century
49.4 x 20.3 cm
Circ.51-1921

291
HEAD of a PANEL, with cusped incised lancets and oculi.
15th century
23.9 x 60.7 cm
Circ.74-1921

292
PANEL, with cross motif filling oculus above and lancets below.
15th century
33.7 x 22.9 cm
Circ.139-1933

293
PORTION of linenfold PANELLING.
15th century
38.8 x 1.2 cm
Circ.156-1928

294
PORTION of linenfold PANELLING, with leaves and fruit (PL.101).
15th century
36.5 x 25 cm
Circ.578-1925

295
PORTION of PANELLING, with imbricated ornament.
Early 16th century
63.5 x 14.6 cm
Circ.65-1936

PLATE 102 Hutch chest with chip-carved decoration (cat. 296)

DOMESTIC

B. FURNITURE

CHESTS AND BOXES

296

CHEST. The front and back are composed of a single panel flanked by broad wedge-shaped standards or stiles, the two front ones of which being curved below on the inner sides so as to form an arch. The end panels slope slightly inwards and are faced with a framework of chamfered rails halved together and tenoned into the standards. The lid, which is a single board, is fitted with a pin hinge, and has rails with curved chamfers on the underside which fit down into slots. On each standard and in the centre of the front is a roundel incised with geometrical patterns:– (1) a simple star within a double zigzag border, (2) seven stars in a single border of zigzags, and (3) a spiral similarly enclosed. Inside the chest

are the grooves into which was fixed the framework of a tray or till with lid, and a well or secret receptacle for money underneath, but there is no slot in the lid. The upper part of the centre roundel has been restored, probably in the 18th century, when an enlarged lock plate was inserted. Each of the roundels is the same size. On the side panels they have had to be pushed right to the edge in order to avoid the line of pegs which secure the flanking stile to the central panel (PL.102).

13th century

50.6 x 109 x 48.2 cm

W.30-1926

Said to have come from a church in Hampshire, this chest is of the hutch type (Eames 1977, pp. 108 & 143-5, and FIG. 17). Apart from the chip-carving there is no decoration, the columns flanking the outer stiles, as at Stoke D'Abernon (FIG.55), Surrey, Midhurst and Bosham, Sussex, being absent here.

FIG 55 St Mary, Stoke D'Abernon, Surrey. Chip-carved 13th century chest.

The museum's chest is a member of a small class of 13th-century hutch chests decorated with standardised chip-carved ornament found mainly in Surrey and Sussex (See Johnston 1907). Most of these chests have pin-hinged lids and a strengthening framework on the sides. The museum's chest is smaller than most and must, like the example at Stoke D'Abernon, have been designed to be easily transportable.

The inflexible manner in which all three roundels are the same size, although there is hardly room for them on the outer stiles, suggests that the carver was using a pre-existing pattern which he could prick onto the surface. Chip-carving, of course,, required only routine skills. Johnston suggested that this family of chests was probably made by the same guild at some central location.

There are traces of red on the roundels of the Stoke D'Abernon chest (Johnston 1907, 273). The application of bright colours to these simple motifs would have been extremely effective.

The hole which has been drilled through the right-hand stile at an angle so that it continues through the upper transom of the side panelling may not be an original feature. If it was for a chain, as a precaution against theft, it would have been less than adequate since the diameter is comparatively small(compare the chains attached to iron straps on the back of the Climping chest (See Johnston, FIG. 19).

297
CHEST; of hutch-type construction, the front has a single panel, grooved above and below, and having three holes for locks (fitted with 18th century lockplates); it is flanked by broad stiles shaped below and grooved; the back is similar to the front; the top has clamps on the underside at either end and is hinged by means of pivots inserted horizontally into the clamps through the back uprights (PL.103).
Given by Sir Edmund Davis
13th century
48.2 x 99 x 38.1 cm
W.158-1921
The chest was purchased by the donor in Surrey, and probably came from a Surrey church. Under

PLATE 103 Hutch chest from a Surrey church (cat. 297)

the terms of the edict of Henry II in 1166 and the papal bull of Innocent III in the reign of King John, church chests, to receive the offerings of the faithful for the crusades, were to be placed in the church, with several locks, of which one was to be in the custody of the priest and the others held by trustworthy parishioners. The usual number of locks, as in this case, was three, the centre one for the priest, the other two for the churchwardens. The money slot in the lid could have been made as part of the above decrees; but the slot in this case appears to be later than the date of the chest, and was probably made so as to adapt the chest, on account of its small size, to a 'Poor Man's Box' or alms box, which became a regular feature in churches under the order of Archbishop Cranmer and other authorities, to meet the distress caused by the dissolution of the monasteries (See Johnston 1907, 301-04).

In any case, it is probable that the hutch-type chests, being of lighter construction than either 'dug-out' or plank chests, were not intended to store plate and valuables. It has been suggested that the 'hutch' chests at All Saints, Hereford and Hereford Cathedral were used to store books (Morgan 1948, 4).

298

CHEST; of hutch-type construction, the front is formed of a single plain panel set in broad stiles slightly shaped below; the back is of similar construction to the front and is united to it at either end by a bar, behind which are the single panels which form the sides. The top, of pine, of 18th century date, is probably a reproduction of the original; it is hinged by means of pivots inserted horizontally through the back uprights and fixed into the clamps on the underside of the lid (PL.104).
13th century
63.5 x 127 x 53.5 cm
W.22-1920
From Great Bedwyn Church, Wiltshire, this chest was figured in Cescinsky and Gribble (1922), FIG.I. The piece is of rough workmanship saw marks being clearly visible on the front panel.

PLATE 104 Hutch chest from Great Bedwyn Church, Wilts (cat. 298)

PLATE 105 Ark chest (cat. 299)

299
CHEST, ark-shaped, composed of horizontal boards mortised into four uprights. The lid, slightly arched and having raised pieces at each end, rotates in grooves cut in the two back uprights (PL.105).
Given by Mr J. Dowell Phillips
Late 13th century type, but possibly 14th or early 15th century
61 x 10 x 45.8 cm
W.21-1913
Ark construction used riven timbers and is illustrated in Macquoid & Edwards (1927), FIG.1. Short of dendrochronology it is impossible to date an object like this with any precision because it lacks any ornamental feature.

300
Carved CHEST front with lock plate reserve, of hutch-type (Eames 1977, 109, FIG.17 & 145); carved with figure subjects in relief; on the left is the Visitation of the Magi, on the right the angels appearing to the shepherds, above is the Coronation of the Virgin, and below, within an arched recess, the Annunciation (PL.106).
About 1430-50
73.6 x 127 cm
W.15-1920
Panel, probably the front of the base or stand of this chest, carved with hounds chasing a stag and a hare.
17.8 x 134 cm
W.15A-1920
Said to have been formerly in Horace Walpole's collection at Strawberry Hill, although there is no definitive evidence for this.
    In the previous catalogue reference was made to

PLATE 106 Carved chest-front with scenes from the Life of the Virgin (cat. 300)

a chest front formerly in the Ypres museum (Casier & Bergmans 1914, PL.XXII). This bears only a superficial resemblance to the museum's panel and serves, if anything, to underline the absence of any stylistic relationship to the latter. The similarity of the carving on the base panel to the decoration of a fourteenth-century chest in Prittlewell Church, Essex (figured by Fred Roe in *Connoisseur*, LVIII, 1920, 45) should encourage us to look for an English model. Indeed, in fourteenth-century English ecclesiastical needlework a number of stylistic and iconographical parallels are evident. Scenes from the Life of the Virgin in mid fourteenth-century vestments such as the Scrope chasuble (New York, Metropolitan Museum) and the Butler Bowden cope (V&A Museum) could have provided the inspiration for our artist. For instance, the arrangement of the angels behind the panel's Coronation of the Virgin is reminiscent of the configuration of cusped arches

which provide the formal framing on the Butler Bowden cope.

The Annunciation to the Shepherds on the apparels in the V&A bearing the shields of Bardolf (Inv.No.8128-1863) has all the elements contained in the same scene on the panel – the angel with scroll emerging from a cloud, the gesturing shepherd on the right (the figure on the panel is damaged), the bag-pipe playing shepherd on the left, and the sheep-dog in the centre.

The carving style of the panel is much later than the embroidery examples cited. From the dress it seems unlikely that the chest was made much before the middle of the fifteenth century. Its apparent iconographical dependence upon earlier English works suggests that it is English. However, a Flemish provenance cannot be ruled out.

301

CHEST or STRONG BOX – 'The Fares Chest' –
constructed of six boards; the front is carved with
two volute-shaped sprays, each ending in a rose,
and in the centre the space for a large lock-plate,
which is missing. On the centre of the back is a band
with the name 'N. FARES in Lombardic capitals,
preceded by a skull-cap and surrounded by a border
of vine and grape ornament. Along the bottom are
three trefoil cusped arches, the spandrels being
filled in with a diaper of rosettes; at each side is a
Gothic buttress. On one end is a monogram formed
of the initials 'N F' surmounted by the skull-cap and
terminating in roses; there is a single arch below, as
on the back. The other end is plain. The lid is
deeply moulded along its front edge. The lid and
hinges are of later date than the sides as is the
arcading underneath the back panel (PL.107a & b).
Given by Mr J. Dowell Phillips
Early 15th century
44.4 x 107 x 45.8 cm
W.20-1913

The presence of decoration on each of the two
main sides is highly unusual in the context of a
normal chest. Yet there can be no doubt that all the
decorative carving is by the same hand. What is
more, on the inside of the back panel are the scars
of the original hinge straps. The lower part of this
panel is lost and has been replaced by the poor-
quality diapered arcading in deal. If allowance is
made for the lost portion the panel would have
been the same height as the front one (35 cm).
Another unusual feature is the considerable thickness of the end pieces; the decorated end's thickness (30 mm.) is particularly excessive given the
quite normal thickness of the front and back
panels. It is legitimate to speculate that the end-
pieces might be the re-used members of some
other object, such as bench-ends. However, their
profile is asymmetrical and therefore quite in-
appropriate for a bench-end. Moreover, they are
perfectly suitable to their positions, which suggests
that the intended front of the chest is the side with
the name on it. The absence of any carving on the
left-hand end suggests that the chest was intended
to stand up against a wall.

The very large space given over to the lock plate
in proportion to the overall size of the front panel
indicates that security was a high priority. This
would seem to corroborate the authenticity of the
extremely thick end-pieces. It has been suggested
that the chest may have been the strong box for a
guild (Cescinsky & Gribble 1922, 24), the legend

'Fares' applying to a place rather than a person. It is
quite clear that, in terms of display, the 'back' panel
was more important than the front. The exposed
end of the chest and the 'back' seem to have acted
as an advertisement. It is more probable that an
individual rather than an institution would publi-
cise a name in this way. The chest is comparatively
small, and therefore portable, but probably stood
about 56 cm higher than it does now.

Several writers have suggested that this piece was
originally a 'counter chest' (See Macquoid & Edwards 1924-27, 146-48, Roe 1916, 129-31 and Symonds
1951, 174). This explains the element of advertisement on the end panel and 'back' of the chest. If
the scars of the hinge-straps on the inside of the
back relate to the original arrangement the top was
always hinged as opposed to having a sliding
mechanism. A hinged lid would have been very
inconvenient as a counter. The functional interpretation of the piece as a counter-chest is, almost
inevitable, however, given the all-round decorative
treatment, the side with the lock, where the
merchant/treasurer sat, having a conspicuously
lesser aesthetic importance.

The quality of the decorative carving on the
chest is high. The stylistic traits on the carving of the
rosettes, for instance, is consistent throughout. The
rosettes do not need to be 'Tudor' or 'Yorkist' as
has been previously suggested. In fact the way that
they are treated with nicks cut in the centre of the
double-flairs of the petals can be paralleled in England in the late fourteenth century as, for instance,
on the choir-stalls of New College, Oxford. The
style of the vine foliage can also be matched closely,
for instance, on the choir-stalls at Nantwich,
Cheshire of about 1400. The decorative Lombardic
lettering used for the legend with prominent serifs
is reminiscent of that on the Studley Bowl (V&A
M.1-1914) a piece of English metalwork of the late
fourteenth century.

302

CHEST, constructed of six boards; the front, which
has traces of the original red paint, is carved with
two bands of ornament, the upper composed of
quatrefoils and trefoils, and the lower of a row of
narrow arches of late Perpendicular character;
below the front is portion of a carved spandrel (the
corresponding spandrel at the other end is missing).
The iron lock plate has been added. The lid and
back, which are of elm, date probably from the
18th century (PL.108).
Given by Mrs. Graham Rees-Mogg

PLATE 107 a & b The 'Fares' chest, front and back view (cat. 301)

PLATE 108 Boarded chest with geometric carving from East Anglia (cat. 302)

About 1500
51 x 114 x 35.5 cm
W.428-1922
East Anglian, purchased by a former owner at Bury St Edmund's.

303
CHEST, constructed of six boards, the front carved in low relief with two cusped ogee arches with roses and leaves in the spandrels. The interior has at one end the slots for a till which is missing. The lid is not the original one (PL.109).
 Given by Mr Sigismund Goetze
About 1500
53.3 x 115 x 40.6 cm
W.98-1922
Said to have come from Warwickshire.

304
CHEST, constructed of six boards; the front is carved with three rows of ornament; below is an arcading, above it a scrolling band with conventional leaves,

and on the top a cresting with rosettes; the ends are plain and have pointed openings below. The lid is not the original one (PL.110).
 Given by Mr Robert L. Mond, F.S.A.
Early 16th century
67.5 x 126 x 48.2 cm
W.69-1916
From a farmhouse in the neighbourhood of Stamford, Lincolnshire. The decoration on the front panel is close to that on another early sixteenth-century chest sold at auction by Christie's in 1968 (See Windisch-Graetz 1982, 225).

305
CHEST; in the front are two panels carved with linenfold pattern; the ends have shaped openings below. Within the chest, at one end, are the grooves for a till, which is missing (PL.111).
 Given by Mr Robert L. Mond, F.S.A.
Early 16th century
55.8 x 83.6 x 35.6 cm
W.85-1921.

PLATE 109 Boarded chest carved with cusped ogee arches (cat. 303)

PLATE 110 Boarded chest carved with three rows of decoration (cat. 304)

PLATE 111 Framed chest with linenfold panelling (cat. 305)

306
TWO PANELS from a CHEST-FRONT, with original painted decoration, carved above with two rosettes and two arches containing tracery, and below with a row of narrow arches.
Given by Mr G. Murray Adams-Acton, through the National Art-Collections Fund
About 1500
H. 39.4 cm, W. of each portion, 48.2 cm
W.4-1928
These panels must have been part of a framed chest front. This technique does not seem to have been applied to domestic furniture much before the middle of the fifteenth century. The technique of chip carving, and the arcaded decoration, are both traditional forms of ornament.

307
PORTION of a CHEST-FRONT, with traces of original red paint;, carved with an arch with rosettes in the spandrels and subdivided into two arches containing conventional tracery.
Given by Mr Murray Adams-Acton, through the National Art-Collections Fund
31.8 x 38.1 cm
About 1500
W.5-1928

308
PORTION of a boarded CHEST-FRONT; below the lock-plate (now missing) is a sexfoil ornament, on one side is a row of interlacing arches filled with bands of spiral ornament, on the other side portions of similar arches (the panel at this point having been mutilated).

Given by Mrs Graham Rees-Mogg
Early 16th century
39.4 x 104 cm
W. 429-1922
East Anglian
Purchased by a former owner at Lavenham, Suffolk.

309
PORTION of a boarded CHEST-FRONT; below the lock-plate (now miss ing) are diagonal bands of ornament; on either side is a rounded arch carved with leaf design and filled with ornament resembling tracery.
Given by Mrs Graham Rees-Mogg
Early 16th century
33 x 96.5 cm
W.430-1922
East Anglia
Purchased by a former owner at Ipswich.

310
COFFER FRONT, with chip-carved circles in two pairs, divided by a plain panel with square aperture at the top for a lock plate, and having trefoil ornament in the spandrels. The design contained within moulded borders. Below the top edge an aperture for a lock plate.
Given by Mr Aymer Vallance
Late 15th century
34.3 cm x 114 cm
W.67-1929

311
COFFER FRONT, carved with tracery arranged in two pairs of arches divided by a geometrical device and having similar ornament in the spandrels. Below the top edge an aperture for a lock plate.
Given by Mr Aymer Vallance
Second half 15th century
33 x 109 cm
W.68-1929

PLATE 112 Framed chest with linenfold panelling (cat. 312)

PLATE 113 Framed chest with 'parchemin' panelling (CAT. 313)

312
FRAMED CHEST with linenfold PANELLING; the lid has
a raised and moulded edge, the front is carved with
three panels of linenfold ornament framed in
moulded stiles. At each end are two more linenfold
panels. Original lock plate removed (PL.112).
Given by Miss Emily Hanson
About 1500
60.3 x 103 x 45 cm
W.28-1930

313
FRAMED CHEST with PANELS of 'parchemin' design;
the two outer panels are carved with bunches of
grapes, the others with foliage; at either end two
panels of linenfold type; plain square feet, plain top,
slightly domed; the lock plate, in the centre of the
top rail in the front, cut in the form of trefoils at the
two bottom corners. Small hole broken through
one of the panels at the right-hand end. Small later
additions to both back feet (PL.113).
Given by Mr F.J. Cleminson
About 1520
72.3 x 131 x 61 cm
W.11-1938
The 'parchemin' decoration is similar to examples
found throughout northern Europe at this time.

CUPBOARDS

314

DESK or CUPBOARD for books. Carved on the back and sides with two rows of Gothic arcading enriched with tracery within a slightly moulded framework; the front is plain with the exception of two carved lions' masks at the upper corners. The framed sloping top opens on hinges, and the interior is fitted with a cupboard with a hinged lid. The lower part of the desk is missing. The lock plate and the book ledge are post-medieval (PL.114a, b & c).

Last quarter of 14th century
97 x 83.8 x 54.6 cm
143-1898

This an extremely rare example of a medieval desk-cum-book cupboard. It is without doubt authentic and English. It is a great pity that it has lost the lower part of its panelling and its base. Two decorative features point strongly to England. The trefoil tracery in the super-arches of the back panel is stilted in the characteristically early Perpendicular way (compare stall-ends at Lincoln Cathedral, See FIG.39). This same trait could also be found on a fragment of panelling from the York Minster choir-

PLATE 114 a, b & c Desk and cupboard for books. General view and details (cat. 314)

FIG 56 a & b Lincoln Cathedral. Lion's mask motif on stall elbow and misericord.

PLATE 114 b & c Details of cat. 314 (Ref. PL. 114a)

stalls in the Roe collection (illustrated in Roe 1910, PL.XVI) where the tracery pattern is sexfoil. The date of the construction of the York stalls is about 1390 (Bond Stalls, 58). The treatment of the lions' masks on the front of the desk is another parallel with Lincoln, in particular the same treatment of the hair in whorls and ear shape (FIGS. 56a & b). The Lincoln stalls must have been manufactured in about 1370 (See CAT.67).

The placing of these masks is reminiscent of the use of this motif on choir-stalls on the standards underneath the capping (compare Chichester Cathedral).

315

LIVERY CUPBOARD. The sides and top are plain, the latter projecting beyond the front. The front has in the centre a hinged door, composed of one panel, grooved at the sides and with two square openings, one above the other, filled with geometrical tracery. The space above the door is occupied by a grooved panel. On each side of the door is a panel grooved like the door and having two upright openings filled with tracery, the square space between them being carved with four trefoils. The cupboard is fitted with two shelves, one across the centre, and the other, a half-shelf, above it. (It's legs, consisting of the prolongation of the ends, are missing). The door hinges are not original and the lock has gone (PL.115).

Given by Mr F. G. Hilton Price, F.S.A., *through the National Art-Collections Fund*

About 1500

9.80 x 45.8 x 64 cm

721-1908

Said to have come from Ivy Church, an old house at Alderbury, near Salisbury. A strong caveat should be entered with regard to the authenticity of this piece. It can be compared to the livery cupboard at St Donat's Castle, Glamorgan (Roe 1902, 101) or the

PLATE 115 Livery cupboard (cat. 315)

cupboards formerly belonging to Morgan Williams (Macquoid 1904, FIGS.2 & 3). The absence of original door hinges and feet leaves little by which to judge the object's genuineness.

316
TWO PANELS, from a cupboard, each carved with three panels of openwork tracery of flamboyant design between which and on the sides are bands of sunk tracery (The lower part of one panel has been cut away). The surface retains traces of the original vermilion colouring (PL.116).
Given by Mr A. W. Leatham
15th century
81.2 and 96.5 x 35.6 cm each
W.37 and 37A-1924
Acquired by the donor from an old house at Syde, Gloucestershire.

317
PANELS, a pair, from the front of a cupboard, each pierced with three panels of tracery, with a fluted band on each side (PL.117).
Given by Mr J. Dowell Phillips
Late 15th or early 16th century
(1) 114 x 40.6 cm, (2) 124 x 41.3 cm
W.36-1913

318
DOOR probably from a BUFFET; in the centre is a rectangular panel containing four vesica-shaped compartments filled in with openwork tracery; the spandrels are decorated with punched foliage ornament; there is a space for a lock (PL.118).
From Sutton Place, Guildford
About 1500
47.00 x 36.4 cm
1973-1900

PLATE 116 Two panels from a cupboard (cat. 316)

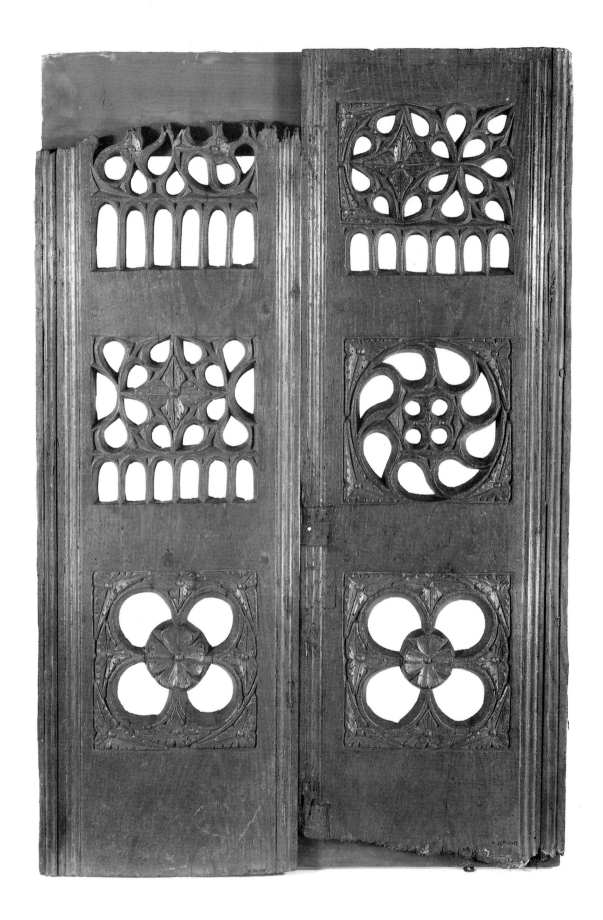

PLATE 117 A pair of panels from a cupboard front (cat. 317)

PLATE 118 Buffet door (cat. 318)

PLATE 119 Side-table or low buffet (cat. 319)

TABLES

319

SIDE-TABLE or LOW BUFFET. The front is arranged as follows: in the centre is an oblong space filled by a modern panel; on each side are two panels of openwork carving, consisting of a crowned 'I H S,' a shield bearing three fleur-de-lys, a rose, and tracery. At either end is a panel of linenfold ornament set horizontally. The bottom rails have channel mouldings, which are continued on the inner sides of the legs and terminate in moulded stops. The top is not the original one, and the framework has been partly restored (PL.119).
Early 16th century
71.0 x 196 X 63.5 cm
W.47-1910
West Country. Macquoid (1904) suggested that this kind of table may have frequently incorporated a draw-leaf mechanism top.

320

TABLE. The top rests on two lower leaves, which are drawn out by levers at each end. The table stands on four square legs, chamfered on the inner sides; these are united above by deep rails with ogee-shaped mouldings, and are connected near to the ground by four plain stretchers, one of which has been restored (PL.120).
From Broadway, near Ilminster, Somerset
Early 16th century
86.2 x 159 cm, open 297 x 81.3 cm
262-1908
See the form (CAT.324), which belongs to this table.

PLATE 120 Table and form from Broadway, Somerset (cat. 320 & 324)

CHAIR

321

ARM-CHAIR. The square back, surmounted at either end by a figure of a crouching lion, has an oblong panel carved with Classical terminal figures ending in scrolls, with two linenfold panels below. The flat arms are enclosed. The front of the box seat has two linenfold panels of simpler form than those on the back; the panelled sides and back of the chair are plain (PL.121).

About 1540

99.2 x 69.8 x 47 cm

W.39-1920

Purchased by the former owner from an old house near Cambridge. Figured in Cescinsky & Gribble (1922), II, 166 and Macquoid and Edwards (1924-27), I, 199, Fig.2.

PLATE 121 Arm-chair (cat. 321)

322
FORM. The framing below the seat is decorated with eight ogee arches, the two central arches further decorated with cusps; the solid supports at either end are buttressed and moulded and have each an ogee arch below; the back framing is missing (PL.122).
From Barningham Hall, Suffolk
Late 15th or early 16th century
53.4 x 236 x 280 cm
W.67-1921

323
FORM, the framing below the seat, which extends beyond the legs, is carved on both sides with ogee-shaped and semi-circular mouldings; the solid legs at either end have grooved edges and arched openings below (Pl.123).
Given by Mr Sigismund Goetze
Early 16th century
45.7 x 155 x 26.8 cm
W. 78-1924

324
FORM. The seat rests on two broad supports with shaped edges, which widen towards the ground, where they terminate in ogee-shaped openings; beneath the seat are two rails with ogee-shaped mouldings. Restored (PL.120 & 124).
Early 16th century or possibly later
53.4 x 165 x 34.3 cm
See Table, CAT.320, to which this form belongs.
263-1908
From Broadway, near Ilminster, Somerset.

325
STOOL. The seat rests on two broad supports with buttressed edges and ogee-shaped openings below; in front, below the seat, is a deep rail with pierced openings; a similar rail at the back is missing (PL.125).
Given by Mr A. Fass
Late 15th or early 16th century
54.6 x 55.8 x 27.8 cm
W.95-1921
Purchased by the donor in Bury St Edmund's.

PLATE 122 Form from Barningham Hall, Suffolk (cat. 322)

PLATE 123 Form with ogee-shaped framing (cat. 323)

PLATE 124 Form from Broadway, Somerset (cat. 324)

PLATE 125 Stool with pierced framing (cat. 325)

326
STOOL. The seat rests on two broad supports with buttressed edges and ogee-shaped openings below; below the seat are two rails with ogee-shaped mouldings (PL.126).
Given by Mr Robert L. Mond, F.S.A.
Early 16th century
55.8 x 55.8 x 33 cm
W.65-1916

327
MODEL of a BENCH or MOVEABLE SETTLE (the back of a carved group), with seated figures of St Anne, the Virgin and Christ; the sides and back of the bench carved with linen-fold panels (PL.127).
Late 15th century
49.5 x 40.6 cm
A.4-1911
East Anglian

PLATE 126 Stool with incised and carved framing (cat. 326)

328
BACK of a WALL BENCH or FIXED SETTLE, composed of seven linenfold panels, in moulded uprights surmounted by carved finials; above the panels is a band of open foliated ornament in spiral borders; the cresting between the finials consists of a series of panels (three of which are missing) carved with Renaissance designs in openwork (PL.128).
The seat belonging to this bench, *Given by Mr Charles Angell*
Early 16th century
113 x 34 cm
W.25-1923
West Country. This is an example of a form with panelled back but without arms which would

make it a settle (compare the extant settle in the abbot's house at Muchelney, Somerset. See FIG.57). Macquoid and Edwards suggest that such an article would have been intended for rooms without fitted wall panelling.

329
CRESTING from the back of a bench, carved in openwork with conventional foliage.
From a Suffolk church.
Given by Mr Frank Jennings
15th century
8.9 x 60.8 cm
W.22-1924.

PLATE 127 Model of a bench or moveable settle (cat. 327)

PLATE 128 Back of a wall bench or fixed settle (cat. 328)

DETAIL OF ARM
TO SEAT

DETAIL OF POSTS

FLOOR

DETAIL OF SEATING ETC IN ABBOT'S ROOM

SCALE   1   2   3   4   FEET

INCHES

LINEN PANELS IN BACK OF SEAT

SCALE FOR DETAILS

INCHES

A STRATTON MENS
P GARRATT DELT

DETAIL OF PIERCED PANEL AT A.

FIG 57 Muchelney Abbey, Somerset. Measured drawing
of settle in abbot's parlour of former abbey (Stratton &
Garratt).

200   *Forms and Stools*

330

TWO PAIRS of POSTS. Each has an octagonal moulded
capital;, a shaft carved with lozenges enclosing
leaves and separated by grooved bands decorated
with notches, and, near the middle, a pomegranate
(the pomegranates on one pair of posts being
represented in seed); and an octagonal moulded
base, the same pair of posts being further carved
with a stop ornament on the four outer angles.
Two posts have grooves into which wainscot
panelling was fitted; on the capitals are iron hooks
and rings (PL.129).
First quarter of 16th century
196 x 10.2 cm
W.18-1911
These are possibly the components of a four-poster
bed (Macquoid and Edwards 1924-27, I, 22 and Cescinsky and Gribble, II, FIGS. 387-390). There was in

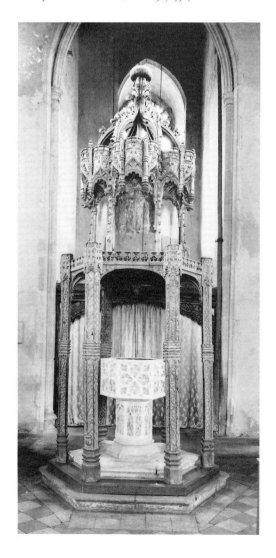

FIG 58 St Botolph, Trunch, Norfolk. Font and cover.

PLATE 129 Set of four posts (cat. 330)

the previous catalogue, it must be said, a regrettable tendency to attribute all the museum's collection of assorted late medieval posts to beds. In fact, we cannot be certain that any of these posts were associated with this category of furniture. Posts were regularly used on screens, and in one case at least on a font, at Trunch, Norfolk (FIG. 58). The presence of mortising and pegging does not prove anything. Perhaps the most telling indicators are the proportions and height of the posts. The height of the plinth is usually greater in proportion to the whole on screen posts than it is in this case.

It was not uncommon in the past for such posts to be assembled with unconnected medieval woodwork to form a medieval 'four-poster'. The Saffron Walden Museum bed (Chinnery 1979, 388) is probably just such a conglomeration of disparate parts. For a discussion of the inventorial evidence for beds in the Middle Ages see Eames 1977, 73-93.

331-333

THREE POSTS – with slight traces of paint (PL.130).
1. Octagonal capital; shaft carved with diagonal bands with a shield on each face bearing respectively a fleur-de-lys, a pomegranate and a rosette (twice); the base fluted in resemblance to Gothic tracery and grooved on one side for the insertion of panelling. 175 x 7 cm
2. Octagonal capital; shaft carved with lozenge ornament enclosing rosettes, fleurs-de-lys and pomegranates, with a shield on each face bearing respectively a pomegranate, a fleur-de-lys, and a rosette (twice); the base fluted. 17 x 7 cm
3. Similar to No. 2, except that one shield bears, instead of a pomegranate, a trefoil of three pearls or berries on a double stem. 164 x 7 cm
Given by J. Dowell Phillips, Esq
First quarter of 16th century
W.22 to W.22B-1913
A trefoil of three pearls or berries on a stalk split at the base, described otherwise as a two-stemmed clover (apparently the same as that on post No. 3) is the merchant's mark of Thomas Paycocke of Coggeshall, Essex (d. 1518), and is carved on the beams of his house at Coggeshall. See Power 1920, 30.

PLATE 130 Three decorated posts (cat. 331-33)

PLATE 131 Two decorated posts (on outside) (cat. 334)   PLATE 131 Decorated post (in centre) (cat. 335)

334
Two Posts, the shafts carved on the upper half with
lozenge ornament enclosing rosettes, and on the
lower with hexagonal diaper pattern. In the
centre, on each face, is a shield bearing a rose (PL.131,
outside).
Early 16th century
189 and 194 x 8.1 cm
W.40 & 40A-1914

335
Post; the upper part carved with lozenge
ornament framing rosettes, the lower with
diamond pattern. In the centre is an octagonal
moulding, the capitals and bases also octagonal
(PL.131, centre).
Early 16th century
194 x 9 cm
W.41-1914

336
Portions of Posts, a pair, with moulded capitals of
hexagonal form, above shafts carved with cavetto
chevron mouldings and quatrefoil bosses. The bases
are carved with the initials T, S (T on the front of
one base, and S on the other), the remaining side
bearing a quatrefoil (PL.132).
About 1520
45.8 x 11.8 x 10 cm
W.33 & 33A-1929

PLATE 132 Portion of posts (cat. 336)

118-1865	97	126-1908	1	Circ.172-1914	211	W.12-1918	119
118A-1865	98	127-1908	2	Circ.174-1914	212	W.38-1918	273
118B-1865	99	128-1908	3	W.40 & 40-1914	334	W.158-1919	203
119-1865	5	198-1908	118	W.41-1914	335	W.159-1919	204
120-1865	6	246-1908	44	W.48-1914	282	Circ.99-1920	150
121-1865	7	252-1908	56	W.48a-1914	283	W.15 & W.15A-1920	300
123-1865	8	262-1908	320	W.49-1914	284	W.22-1920	298
124-1865	9	263-1908	324	W.51-1914	17	W.39-1920	321
377-1890	87	721-1908	315	W.51C-1914	18	W.42-1920	239
539-1892	270	A.14-1909	243	W.51D-1914	19	Circ.26-1921	179
511-1893	123	W.6-1909	241	W.51E-1914	20	Circ.36-1921	170
23-1894	100	W.7-1909	242	W.51F-1914	21	Circ.37-1921	180
24-1894	101	A.1-1910	42	W.51I-1914	22	Circ.38-1921	181
754-1895	254	Circ.216-1910	151	W.51J-1914	23	Circ.39-1921	183
150,150A & 150B-1897	238	W.14-1910	200	W.76-1914	221	Circ.41-1921	182
152-1897	91	W.47-1910	319	W.76A-1914	222	Circ.44-1921	287
214-1897	55	W.82-1910	95	W.76B-1914	223	Circ.48-1921	288
218-1897	213	A.4-1911	327	W.76C-1914	224	Circ.49-1921	289
221 to 221R-1897	237	Circ.296-1911	263	76D-1914	225	Circ.51-1921	290
236-1897	90	W.5-1911	234	76E-1914	226	Circ.64-1921	146
143-1898	314	W.6-1911	235	76F-1914	227	Circ.67-1921	152
488-1898	285	W.18-1911	330	76G-1914	228	Circ.74-1921	291
499-1898	148	W.21-1911	38	76H-1914	229	Circ.76-1921	147
574-1898	192	W.22-1911	39	76I-1914	230	Circ.87-1921	35
1966-1900	256	W.23-1911	40	76J-1914	231	Circ.88-1921	36
1969 to 1969F-1900	262	W.24-1911	41	76K-1914	232	Circ.93-1921	265
1967-1900	259	W.25-1911	68	W.2-1916	169	W.6-1921	73
1968-1900	250	W.66-1911	244	W.3-1916	160	W.7-1921	69
1969 to 1969F-1900	262	W.91-1911	195	W.4-1916	165	W.8-1921	70
1970-1900	153	W.94-1911	184	W.5-1916	161	W.9-1921	74
1972 & 1972A-1900	154	W.95-1911	185	W.6-1916	159	W.10-1921	75
1973-1900	318	W.34-1912	62	W.7-1916	162	W.11-1921	76
1974 & 1974A-1900	286	W.34A-1912	63	W.8-1916	163	W.12-1921	77
587-1901	261	W.34B-1912	64	W.9-1916	164	W.14-1921	168
668-1902	218	W.34C-1912	65	W.10-1916	166	W.16-1921	158
669A-1902	219	W.48-1912	66	W.11-1916	167	W.17-1921	171
670-1902	220	A.25-1913	249	W.12-1916	129	W.18-1921	172
725-1902	255	W.17-1913	201	W.13-1916	130	W.19-1921	191
726-1902	247	W.18-1913	202	W.16-1916	10	W.20-1921	173
727-1902	248	W.20-1913	301	W.17-1916	11	W.21-1921	89
661-1904	271	W.21-1913	299	W.18-1916	12	W.23-1921	128
1152-1904	43	W.22-1913	331	W.19-1916	121	W.24 & W.24A-1921	132
368-1905	253	W.22A-1913	332	W.20-1916	120	W.25-1921	29
271-1906	103	W.22B-1913	333	W.21-1916	272	W.26-1921	45
299-1907	186	W.35-1913	267	W.65-1916	326	W.27-1921	236
118-1908	24	W.36-1913	317	W.68-1916	251	W.28 to W.37-1921	260
119-1908	25	W.57-1913	252	W.69-1916	304	W.42-1921	276
120-1908	26	W.59-1913	245	W.11-1917	28	W.50-1921	93
121-1908	27	Circ.170-1914	210	A.86-1918	246	W.52-1921	71

W.53-1921	72	W.200-1923	198	W.6-1928	240
W.54-1921	78	W.5-1924	138	W.7-1928	48
W.55-1921	194	W.6-1924	134	W.39-1928	281
W.56-1921	174	W.7-1924	135	W.40-1928	280
W.57-1921	175	W.9-1924	136	W.43-1928	208
W.58-1921	176	W.10-1924	137	W.54-1928	102
W.59-1921	177	W.11-1924	139	W.33 & W.33A-1929	336
W.60-1921	178	W.12-1924	133	W.67-1929	310
W.62-1921	260	W.13-1924	258	W.68-1929	311
W.63-1921	264	W.14-1924	112	W.69-1929	92
W.64-1921	274	W.15-1924	113	W.70-1929	52
W.65-1921	275	W.16-1924	114	W.71-1929	53
W.66-1921	278	W.18-1924	115	W.72-1929	54
W.67-1921	322	W.19-1924	205	W.74-1929	156
W.85-1921	305	W.20-1924	206	W.4-1930	88
W.93-1921	265	W.21-1924	207	W.5-1930	46
W.95-1921	325	W.22-1924	329	W.6-1930	47
W.145-1921	51	W.23-1924	110	W.8-1930	277
W.148-1921	108	W.26-1924	111	W.28-1930	312
W.149-1921	104	W.27 to W.30-1924	140	W.10-1931	37
W.150 & W.150A-1921	131	W.34-1924	14	W.53-1931	233
W.151-1921	126	W.35-1924	15	Circ.139-1933	292
W.153-1921	279	W.36-1924	16	W.39-1934	214
W.158-1921	297	W.37 & W.37A-1924	316	Circ.65-1936	295
W.98-1922	303	W.69-1924	257	W.10-1936	149
W.412-1922	109	W.74-1924	187	W.11-1938	313
W.413-1922	127	W.75-1924	188	W.63-1938	157
W.418-1922	193	W.76-1924	189	W.1-1946	266
W.419-1922	122	W.77-1924	190	W.4-1948	79
W.420-1922	107	W.78-1924	323	W.5-1948	80
W.428-1922	302	W.92-1924	196	W.6-1948	81
W.429-1922	308	W.102-1924	96	W.7-1948	82
W.430-1922	309	W.104-1924	67	W.8-1948	83
W.534-1922	124	W.108-1924	105	W.9-1948	84
W.535-1922	125	W.109-1924	106	W.10-1948	85
W.23-1923	50	W.110-1924	141	W.11-1948	86
W.25-1923	328	Circ.578-1925	294	W.8-1958	215
W.29-1923	199	W.57 & W.57A-1925	49	W.9-1958	216
W.172-1923	13	Circ.1222-1926	4	W.10-1958	21
W.187-1923	142	W.28 & 28A-1926	209		
W.188-1923	143	W.30-1926	296		
W.189-1923	144	W.107-1926	30		
W.190-1923	145	W.108-1926	31		
W.191-1923	116	W.34-1927	269		
W.195-1923	117	Circ.156-1928	293		
W.196-1923	32	W.2-1928	268		
W.197-1923	33	W.3-1928	94		
W.198-1923	34	W.4-1928	306		
W.199-1923	197	W.5-1928	307		

ABBREVIATIONS AND SELECT BIBLIOGRAPHY

Proc.Soc.Antiq
Proceedings of the Society of Antiquaries

Arch.Camb
Archaeologia Cambrensis

Arch.Jnl
Archaeological Journal

Archaeol
Archaeologia

B.A.A.Jnl
Journal of the British Archaeological Association

B.A.R
British Archaeological Reports

B.G.A.S
Transactions of the Bristol and Gloucestershire Archaeological
Society

B.L
British Library

B.O.E
Buildings of England Series

Proc.Camb.Antiq.Soc
Proceedings of the Cambridge Antiquarian Society

R.C.H.M
Royal Commission on Historical Monuments

L.A.M.A.S
London and Middlesex Archaeological Society

Proc.Soc.Ant.Scot
Proceedings of the Society of Antiquaries of Scotland

R.I.B.A.
Royal Institute of British Architects

Suss.Arch.Coll
Sussex Archaeological Collections

S.I.A
Suffolk Institute of Archaeology and Natural History Procs

V.C.H
Victoria County History Series

W.C.R
Winchester Cathedral Record

UNPUBLISHED DOCUMENTARY SOURCES

Crallan
F.A. Crallan, Manuscript notes and sketches. Library of the Council
for the Care of Churches.

Coldstream (1973)
Nicola Coldstream, The Development of Flowing Tracery in
Yorkshire *c.* 1300-1370, Unpublished Ph.D. Thesis, Courtauld
Institute of Art, University of London, 1973.

Grössinger (1972)
Christa Grössinger, 'Eine Studie für der stilgeschichtlichen
Entwicklung englischer Miserkordien in 13 und 14 Jahrhundert',
Ph.D.thesis, Vienna University Dissertation, 1972.

Tracy (1984)
Charles Tracy, English Gothic Choir-Stalls to *c.* 1400, Ph.D. Thesis,
Courtauld Institute of Art, University of London, 1984.

PUBLISHED BOOKS AND ARTICLES

Anderson (1935)
L.M.D. Anderson, *The Medieval Carver*, Cambridge, 1935.

Anderson (1938)
L.M.D. Anderson, *Animal Carvings in British Churches*, Cambridge, 1938.

Anderson (1954)
L.M.D. Anderson, *Misericords. Medieval Life in English Woodcarving*,
Harmondsworth, 1954.

Anderson (1959)
L.M.D. Anderson, 'Twelfth century design sources of Worcester
Cathedral misericords', *Archaeol.*, XCVII, 1959, 165-78.

Anderson (1967)
L.M.D. Anderson, 'The Choir Stalls of Lincoln Minster', Lincoln,
1967.

Anderson (1969)
L.M.D. Anderson, Essay in Remnant's, *Catalogue of Misericords* (See
below)

Architectural Museum (1877)
Catalogue of the Royal Architectural Museum, 1877.

Ashworth (1852)
Edward Ashworth, 'On the Woodwork of Exeter Cathedral',*Trans.
Exeter Diocesan Architectural Society*, IV, 1853, 323-331.

Baker King (1874)
C.R. Baker King, 'Choir Fittings in Rochester Cathedral', *Spring
Gardens Note Book*, London, 1874, Vol. II, 74-76.

Barber (1903)
E. Barber, 'Chester Cathedral: The Stalls, Misereres, and Woodwork of the Choir', *Chester and North Wales Archaeological and Historical Society*, 9 (New Series), 1903, 46-58.

Bennett (1982)
A. Bennett, Review of Sandler (1974) in *Art Bulletin*, LXIV, No.3, September 1982, 502-8.

Beloe (1900)
Edward M. Beloe, *Our Churches: (King's Lynn, Norfolk)*, Cambridge, 1900.

Bilson (1920)
John Bilson, 'St Mary's Church, Beverley', *Yorkshire Archaeological Journal*, XXV, 1920, 357-436.

Bilson (1926)
John Bilson, 'St Mary's Church, Beverley', *Yorkshire Archaeological Journal*, XXVIII, 1926, 340.

Bond (Fonts)
Francis Bond, *Fonts and Font Covers*, 1908.

Bond (Screens)
Francis Bond, *Screens and Galleries in English Churches*, Oxford, 1908.

Bond (Misericords)
Francis Bond, *Wood Carvings in English Churches: I.Misericords*, London, 1910.

Bond (Stalls)
Francis Bond, *Wood Carvings in English Churches: I.Stalls and Tabernacle Work and II. Bishops' Thrones and Chancel Chairs*, London, 1910.

F. Bligh Bond (1908)
F. Bligh Bond, 'On the Roodscreens in Cambridgeshire', *Proc.Camb.Antiq.Soc.*, 1908, 31-75.

Bond & Camm (1909)
F. Bligh Bond and B. Camm, *English Church Screens and Roodlofts*, 2 vols., London, 1909.

Bony (1979)
J. Bony, *The English Decorated Style*, Oxford, 1979.

Borenius and Tristram (1928)
T. Borenius & E. W. Tristram, 'A Early English Picture', *Apollo*, March, 1928, 125-26.

Boucher (1976)
F. Boucher, 'Micro-Architecture as the 'idea' of Gothic Theory and Style', *Gesta*, XV, 1976, 71-89.

Brakspear (1913)
H. Brakspear, 'Malmesbury Abbey', *Archaeol.*, LXIV, 1913, 422.

Brandon (1849)
R. and J.A. Brandon, *An Analysis of Gothick Architecture*, 2 Vols, London, 1849.

Brassington (1925)
W.S. Brassington, 'Worle, Woodspring Priory and Kewstoke', *Somerset Arch. and Nat.Hist.Soc., Bath Branch Proc.*, 1925, 55.

Briggs (1925)
M.S. Briggs, *A Short History of the Buildings Crafts*, Oxford, 1925.

B.O.E. (*Cambridgeshire*)
Nikolaus Pevsner, B.O.E., *Cambridgeshire*, London, 1970.

B.O.E. (*Herefordshire*)
Nikolaus Pevsner, B.O.E., *Herefordshire*, London, 1963.

B.O.E. (*Hertfordshire*)
Nikolaus Pevsner (Revd Bridget Cherry), B.O.E., *Hertfordshire*, London, 1977.

B.O.E. (*Nottinghamshire*)
Nikolaus Pevsner, Revd Elizabeth Williamson, B.O.E., *Nottinghamshire*, London, 1979.

B.O.E. (*South Devon*)
Nikolaus Pevsner, B.O.E., *South Devon*, London, 1952

B.O.E. (*Suffolk*)
Nikolaus Pevsner, Revd Enid Radcliffe, B.O.E., *Suffolk*, London, 1974.

Carpenter-Turner (1967)
W.J. Carpenter-Turner, 'Winchester Choir Stalls', *Hampshire Chronicle*, January 14th., 21st. and 28th., 1967.

Carter (1780)
John Carter, *Specimens of the Ancient Sculpture and Paintings now remaining in this kingsom etc.*, London, 1780.

Casier and Bergmans (1914)
Joseph Casier and Paul Bergmans, *L'Art Ancien dans les Flandres*, Brussels and Paris, 1914.

Cautley (1937)
H.M. Cautley, *Suffolk Churches and their Treasures*, London, 1937.

Cautley (1949)
H.M. Cautley, *Norfolk Churches*, Ipswich, 1949.

Cave (1943)
C.J.P. Cave, 'Carvings in the Spandrels of the Quire Stalls', *Winchester Cathedral Record*, 1943, 4,5.

Cescinsky and Gribble (1922)
H. Cescinsky and E.R. Gribble, *Early English Furniture and Woodwork*, 2 vols, London, 1922.

Chanter (1932)
J.F. Chanter, *The Bishop's Palace Exeter*, London, 1932.

Chatwin (1928)
P.B. Chatwin, 'The Decoration of the Beauchamp Chapel, Warwick, with special reference to the Sculptures', *Archaeol.*, LXXVII, 1928, 316-17.

Cheetham (1984)
Francis Cheetham, *English Medieval Alabasters*, Oxford, 1984.

Chinnery 1979.
Victor Chinnery, *Oak Furniture. The British Tradition*, Woodbridge, 1979.

Church (1907)
C.M. Church, 'The Prebendal Stalls and Misericords in the Cathedral church of Wells', *Archaeol.*, LV, 1907, 319-42.

Clarke (1920)
K.M. Clarke, 'Misericords of Exeter Cathedral', *Devon and Cornwall Notes and Queries*, XI, II, 1920, 1-54.

Cobb (1980)
Gerald Cobb, *English Cathedrals, The Forgotten Centuries*, London, 1980.

Cochet (1875)
Cochet, *Catalogue du Musée des Antiquités*, Rouen, 1875.

Colchester (1975)
L.S. Colchester, 'A Picture Book of the Misericords of Wells Cathedral', Wells, 1975.

Colling (1848-50)
J.K. Colling, *Gothic Ornaments*, 2 Vols, London, 1848-50.

Colling (1874)
J.K. Colling, *English Mediaeval Foliage*, London, 1874.

Colvin (1963)
H.M. Colvin (ed.), *The History of the King's Works*, Vol. I, London, 1963.

Constable (1928)
W.G. Constable, 'Some Devonshire Rood Screen Paintings', *Connoisseur*, LXXX, April 1928, 195-205 and LXXXI, May 1928, 3-9.

Constable (1929)
W.G. Constable, 'Some East Anglian Rood Screen Paintings', *The Connoisseur*, LXXXIV, Sept. 1929, 141-47; Oct. 1929, 211-20; Nov.1929, 290-94; Dec.1929, 358-65.

Corder (1918)
J.S. Corder, 'Notes on Bury Corner Posts', S.I.A., 1918, 94 & Pl.8.

Corry (1974)
Percy Newton Corry, 'The Quire and Misericords of St Mary's Parish Church, Nantwich, Cheshire', Nantwich, 1974.

Cox (1907)
J.C. Cox, *English Church Furniture*, London, 1907.

Cox (1915)
J.C. Cox, *Pulpits, Lecterns and Organs in English Churches*, Oxford, 1915.

Cox (1916)
J.C. Cox, *Bench ends in English Churches*, Oxford, 1916.

Cox (1923)
J.C. Cox, *English Church Fittings, Furniture and Accessories* (with an introduction by A. Vallance), London, 1923.

Cox & Harvey (1907)
J.C. Cox and A. Harvey, *English Church Furniture*, London, 1907.

Crallan 1897.
F.A. Crallan, *Details of Gothic Woodcarving*, London, 1896.

Crossley (1916)
F.H. Crossley, 'Stallwork in Cheshire', *Trans Hist. Soc. of Lancs and Cheshire*, LXVIII, 1916, 85-106.

Crossley (1917)
F.H. Crossley, 'The Church Screens of Cheshire', *Trans Hist. Soc. of Lancs and Cheshire*, LXIX, 1917, 1-53.

Crossley (1919)
F.H. Crossley, 'On the Remains of Medieval Stallwork in Lancashire', *Trans Hist. Soc. of Lancs and Cheshire*, LXX, 1918, 1-42.

Crossley (1941)
F.H. Crossley, *English Church Craftsmanship*, London, 1941.

Crossley & Ridgway (1943 *et seqq.*)
Fred H. Crossley and Maudie H. Ridgway, 'Screens, Lofts and Stalls situated in Wales and Monmouthshire', *Arch.Camb.*: .DS
'Part I. Introduction', XCVII, 2, 1943, 135-60.
'Part II. Anglesey and Caernarvonshire', XCVIII, 1, 1944, 64-112.
'Part III. Merioneth and Flintshire', XCVIII, 2, 1945, 153-98.
'Part IV. Denbighshire and Cardiganshire', XCIX, 1, 1946, 1-56.
'Part V. Montgomeryshire and Carmarthenshire', XCIX, 2, 1947, 179-230.
'Part VI. Radnorshire', XCX, 1, 1948, 207-51.
'Part VII. Brecknockshire', CII, 1, 1952, 48-82.
'Part VIII. Pembrokeshire', CVI, 1957, 9-45.
'Part IX. Glamorgan', CVII, 1958, 72-108.
'Part XI. Border influences; Additions and Corrections *etc*'., CXI, 1962, 59-102.

Dell (1905)
R. Dell, 'A Tudor Manor House: Sutton Place by Guildford', *The Burlington Magazine*, VII, 1905, 289-301.

Druce (1911)
G.C. Druce, 'Notes on the History of the Heraldic Jall or Yale', *Arch.Jnl*, LXVIII, 1911, 173-99.

Druce (1913)
G.C. Druce, 'Animals in English Woodcarvings', *Walpole Soc.*, III, 1913-14, 58-73.

Druce (1917)
G.C. Druce, 'The Carvings of the Stalls, St Katherine's Chapel, Regent's Park', L.A.M.A.S. Trans, N.S.3, 1917, 3-27.

Druce (1931)
G.C. Druce, 'Misericords: Their form and decoration', B.A.A.Jnl, N.S. XXXVI, 1931, 244-64.

Druce (1938)
G.C. Druce, 'Stalls and Misericords in Hertfordshire Churches', East Herts Arch. Assn, 1938, 131-40.

Druce (1939)
G.C. Druce, 'Stall Carvings in the Church of St Mary of Charity, Faversham', Arch.Cantiana, L, 1939, 11-32.

Eames (1971)
P. Eames, 'Documentary Evidence concerning the character and use of Domestic Furnishings in England in the fourteenth and fifteenth centuries', Furniture History, VII, 1971, 41-60.

Eames (1973)
P. Eames, 'Inventories as sources of evidence for domestic furnishings in the fourteenth and fifteenth centuries', Furniture History, IX, 1973, 33-40.

Eames (1977)
P. Eames, Furniture in England, France and the Netherlands from the Twelfth to the Fifteenth Century, London, 1977.

Eeles (1956)
Francis C. Eeles, King's College Chapel, Aberdeen, Edinburgh and London, 1956.

Egbert (1967)
Virginia W. Egbert, The Mediaeval Artist at Work, New Jersey, 1967.

Elwes & Henry (1907)
H.J. Elwes A. Henry, The Trees of Great Britain and Ireland: II. Common Oak, Edinburgh, 1907.

Erskine (1981 & 1983)
Audrey M. Erskine, 'The Accounts of the Fabric of Exeter Cathedral, 1279-1353', Part I: 1279-1326, Part II: 1328-53, Devon and Cornwall Record Society, N.S.. Part I: Vol.24, 1981; Part II: Vol.26, 1983.

Fox (1890)
G.E. Fox, 'Notes on painted screens and roofs in Norfolk', Arch.Jnl, XLVI, 1890, 65-77.

Fox (1906)
G.E. Fox, 'Medieval Painting', in V.C.H., Norfolk, II, London, 1906, 529-54.

A. Gardner (1935)
Arthur Gardner, A handbook of English Medieval Sculpture, Cambridge, 1935.

A. Gardner (1940)
Arthur Gardner, Alabaster Tombs of the Pre-Reformation Period in England, Cambridge, 1940.

A. Gardner (1951)
Arthur Gardner, English Medieval Sculpture, 2nd ed., Cambridge, 1951.

A. Gardner (1958)
A. Gardner, Minor English Wood Sculpture 1400-1550, London, 1958.

S. Gardner (1927)
S. Gardner, English Gothic Foliage Sculpture, Cambridge, 1927.

Glasscoe & Swanton (1978)
Marion Glasscoe and Michael Swanton, 'Medieval Woodwork in Exeter Cathedral', Exeter, 1978.

A. Goodman (1927)
A.W. Goodman, 'The Choir Stalls, Winchester Cathedral', Arch. Jnl., LXXXIV, 1927, 125-28.

W.L. Goodman (1964)
W.L. Goodman, A History of Woodworking Tools, London, 1964.

W.L. Goodman (1962)
W.L. Goodman, Woodwork, Oxford, 1962.

Goulbourn & Symonds (1876)
E.M. Goulbourn and H. Symonds, The Ancient Sculpture on the Roof of Norwich Cathedral, London and Norwich, 1876.

Grössinger (1975)
Christa Grössinger, 'English Misericords of the Thirteenth and Fourteenth Centuries and their relationship to manuscript illuminations', Jnl. of the Warburg and Courtauld Institutes, XXXVIII, London, 1975, 97-108..

Harrison (1893)
F. Harrison, Annals of an old Manor House, Sutton Place, Guildford, London, 1893.

Hart (1894)
C.J. Hart, 'Old Chests', Birmingham and Midlands Inst.Trans, 1894, 60-94.

Harvey (1936)
John H. Harvey, 'Master Hugh Herland, Chief Carpenter to King Richard II', Connoisseur, June 1936.

Harvey (1938)
John H. Harvey, 'The Mediaeval Carpenter and his work as an Architect', R.I.B.A.Jnl, 3rd ser., XLV, June 1938, 733-43.

Harvey (1948)
John H. Harvey, 'The King's Chief Carpenters', B.A.A.Jnl, XI, 1948, 13-34.

Harvey (1975)
John H. Harvey, Mediaeval Craftsmen, London, 1975.

Harvey (1978)
John H. Harvey, The Perpendicular Style, 1330-1485, London, 1978.

Harvey (1982)
John H. Harvey, 'The Building of Wells Cathedral, II: 1307-1508', from *Wells Cathedral: A History*, (ed. L.S. Colchester), Shepton Mallet, 1982, 76-101.

Harvey (1984)
John H. Harvey, *English Mediaeval Architects*, London, Revd Ed., 1984.

Hastings (1955)
Maurice Hastings, *St Stephen's Chapel and its place in the development of the Perpendicular Style in England*, Cambridge, 1955.

Havard (1887-90)
Henry Havard, *Dictionnaire de l'ameublement et de la décoration, depuis le XIIIe siècle jusqu'a nos jours*, I-IV, Paris, 1887-90.

Hayward (1965)
H. Hayward (ed.), *World Furniture*, London, 1965.

Hewett (1969)
C.A. Hewett, *The Development of Carpentry 1200-1700. An Essex Study*, Newton Abbot, 1969.

Hewett (1974)
C.A. Hewett, *English Cathedral Carpentry*, London, 1974.

Hewett (1974a)
C.A. Hewett, *Church Carpentry. A Study based on Essex examples*, London, 1974.

Hewett (1980)
C.A. Hewett, *English Historic Carpentry*, London, 1980.

Hewett (1985)
C.A. Hewett, *English Cathedral and Monastic Carpentry*, Chichester, 1985.

Hibben (1933)
T. Hibben, *The Carpenter's Tool Chest*, London, 1933.

Hildburgh (1923-4)
W. L. Hildburgh, 'An Alabaster Table of the Annunciation with the Crucifix: a Study in English Iconography', *Archaeol*, LXXIV, 1923-4, 203-32.

Hope (1900)
W. St John Hope, *The Architectural History of the Church and Monastery of St. Andrew, Rochester*, London, 1900.

Hope (1901)
W. St John Hope, *The Stall Plates of the Knights of the Order of the Garter. 1348-1485*, London, 1901.

Hope (1913)
W. St John Hope, *Windsor Castle, An Architectural History*, 2 vols., London, 1913.

Hope (1917)
W. St John Hope, 'Quire Screens in English Churches with Special Reference to the Twelfth Century Quire Screen formerly in the Cathedral Church of Ely', *Archaeol.*, LXVIII, 1917, 44-110.

Howard (1876)
J.J. Howard (ed.), 'The Visitation of Suffolke, made by William Hervey', II, London, 1876.

Howard and Crossley (1917)
Frank E. Howard and F.H. Crossley, *English Church Woodwork. 1250-1550.*, London, 1917.

Hudson (1924)
H.A. Hudson, *The Medieval Woodwork in Manchester Cathedral*, Manchester, 1924.

Jeavons (1947-48)
S.A. Jeavons, 'Medieval Stallwork in South Staffordshire', *Birmingham Arch.Jnl*, LXVII-LXVIII, 1947-48, 42-54.

Jervis (1976)
Simon Jervis, 'Woodwork of Winchester Cathedral', Winchester, 1976.

Johnston (1907)
P.M. Johnston, 'Church Chests of the Twelfth and Thirteenth Centuries in England', *Arch.Jnl*, LXIV, 1907, 243-306.

Joy (1964)
Edward T. Joy, 'Woodwork in Winchester Cathedral', Winchester, 1964.

Jupp & Pocock (1887)
E.B. Jupp and W.W. Pocock, *An Historical Account of the Worshipful Company of Carpenters of the City of London*, London, 1887.

Kelly (1934)
William Kelly, 'Carved Oak from St Nicholas Church, Aberdeen', *Soc.Ant.Scot.Proc.*, LXVIII, 1934, 355-65.

Keyser (1883)
C.E. Keyser, *A List of Buildings in Great Britain and Ireland having Mural and other Painted Decorations*, 3rd ed., London, 1883.

Keyser (1898)
C.E. Keyser, 'On the Panel Paintings of Saints in the Devonshire Screens', *Archaeol*, 2nd Ser., VI, 1898, 183-222.

King (1963)
Donald King. *Opus Anglicanum. English Medieval Embroidery*, Arts Council Exhibition Catalogue, London, 1963.

Laird (1986)
Marshall Laird, *English Misericords*, London, 1986.

Lasko & Morgan (1974)
P. Lasko and N.J. Morgan (ed.), *Medieval Art in East Anglia 1300-1520*, London, 1974.

Lethaby (1906)
W.R. Lethaby, *Westminster Abbey and the King's Craftsmen*, London, 1906.

Lethaby (1925)
W.R. Lethaby, *Westminster Abbey re-examined*, London, 1925.

Lewer (1913)
H. William Lewer and J. Charles Wall, *The Church Chests of Essex*, London, 1913.

Lillie (1928-36)
W.W. Lillie, 'Screenwork in the County of Suffolk', *Suffolk Inst.of Archaeol. and Nat.Hist.Proc.*, XX-XXII, 1928-36.

Long (1929)
E.T. Long, 'The Church Screens of Dorset', *Arch.Jnl*, 2nd Ser., XXXI (1924), 1929, 127-61.

Macpherson (1889)
Norman Macpherson, *Notes on the chapel, crown and other ancient buildings of King's College, Aberdeen*, Edinburgh, 1889.

Macquoid (1904)
Percy Macquoid, *A History of English Furniture: Vol.I. The Age of Oak*, London, 1904.

Macquoid & Edwards (1924-27)
Percy Macquoid and Ralph Edwards, *The Dictionary of English Furniture from the Middle Ages to the late Georgian Period*, 3 vols, London, I & II, 1924; III, 1927.

Maffei
E. Maffei, *Le Mobilier Civil en Belgique au Moyen Âge*, Namur, *n.d.*.

Maskell (1911)
Alfred Maskell, *Wood Sculpture*, London, 1911.

Mercer (1969)
E. Mercer, *Furniture 700-1700*, London, 1969.

Morgan (1948)
F.C. Morgan, 'Church Chests of Herefordshire', Hereford, 1948 (reprinted from *Woolhope Club Trans*, 1947).

Morris (1978)
Richard K. Morris, 'The Development of later Gothic mouldings in England *c.* 1250-1400. Part I', *Architectural History*, 21, 1978, 18-57.

Neale (1877)
James Neale, *The Abbey Church of St Alban, Hertfordshire*, London, 1877.

Oliver (1912)
Basil Oliver, *Old Houses and Village Buildings in East Anglia*, London, 1912.

Palmer (1953)
W. Palmer, 'The Coronation Chair', H.M.S.O., 1953.

Parker (1850)
J.H. Parker, *A Glossary of Terms used in Grecian, Roman, Italian and Gothic Architecture*, 5th ed., Oxford and London, 1850.

Parker (1851)
J.H. Parker, *Domestic Architecture in England from the Conquest to the thirteenth century*, Oxford, 1851.

Peacock (1866)
Edward Peacock, *English Church Furniture, Ornaments and Decoration at the Period of the Reformation*, 1866.

Phipson (1896)
E. Phipson, *Choir Stalls and their Carvings*, London, 1896.

Pigott (1869)
J. Pigott, 'Rood Screens of East Anglia', *Proc.Camb.Ant.Soc.*, 1st Ser., III, 1869, 28.

Pollen (1874)
John H. Pollen, *Ancient and Modern Furniture and Woodwork in the South Kensington Museum*, London, 1874.

Power (1920)
E. Power, *The Paycockes of Coggeshall*, London, 1920.

Prior and Gardner (1912)
E.S. Prior and A. Gardner, *An Account of Medieval Figure Sculpture in England*, Cambridge, 1912.

A .C. Pugin (1831)
A.C. Pugin, *Examples of Gothic Architecture*, London, 1831.

A.W.N. Pugin (1835)
A.W.N. Pugin, *Gothic furniture in the style of the fifteenth century*, London, 1835.

A.W.N. Pugin (1836)
A.W.N. Pugin, *Details of Antient Timber Houses etc.*, London, 1836.

A.W.N. Pugin (1843)
A. W. Pugin, *An Apology for the Revival of Christian Architecture in England*, London, 1843.

A.W.N. Pugin (1844)
A.W.N. Pugin, *Fifteenth and Sixteenth Century Ornaments*, Edinburgh, 1844.

A.W.N. Pugin (1846)
A.W.N. Pugin. *Glossary of Ecclesiastical Ornament and Costume*, 2 vols, London, 1846.

A.W.N. Pugin (1851)
A.W.N. Pugin, *A Treatise on Chancel Screens and Rood Lofts*, London, 1851.

Purvis (1929)
J.S. Purvis, 'The Ripon Carvers and the lost choir-stalls of Bridlington Priory', *Yorkshire Arch.Jnl*, XXIX, 1929, 157-201.

Purvis (1935)
J.S. Purvis, 'The Use of Continental Woodcuts and Prints by the Ripon School of Woodcarvers', *Archaeol.*, LXXXV, 1935, 107-28.

Remnant (1969)
G.L. Remnant (with an introduction by L.M.D. Anderson), *A Catalogue of Misericords in Great Britain*, Oxford, 1969.

Remnant & Steer (1961)
G.L. Remnant and F.W. Steer, 'Misericords in Chichester Cathedral', *The Chichester Papers No. 22*, Chichester, 1961.

Remnant & Steer (1962)
G.L. Remnant and F.W. Steer, 'Misericords in St Mary's Hospital, Chichester', *The Chichester Papers No. 28*, Chichester, 1962.

Rickert (1965)
M. Rickert, *Painting in Britain. The Middle Ages*, Oxford, 1965.

Robinson (1905)
F.S. Robinson, *English Furniture*, London, 1905.

Roe (1902)
Fred Roe, *Ancient Coffers and Cupboards*, London, 1902.

Roe (1905)
Fred Roe, *Old Oak Furniture*, London, 1905.

Roe (1916)
Fred Roe, 'The Art of the Cofferer II – Decoration', *Connoisseur*, XLIV, 1916, 123-34.

Roe (1920)
Fred Roe, *A History of Oak Furniture*, London, 1920.

Roe (1928)
Fred Roe, *Ancient Church Chests and Chairs in the Home Counties*, London, 1928.

Roe (1928a)
Fred Roe, 'Mediaeval Woodwork from South Kensington', *Connoisseur*, LXXXI, May 1928, 60.

Rushforth (1936)
G. McN. Rushforth, *Medieval Christian Imagery*, Oxford, 1936.

Salzman (1952)
L.F. Salzman, *Building in England down to 1540 – A Documentary History*, Oxford, 1952.

Sandler (1974)
L.F. Sandler, *The Peterborough Psalter in Brussels and other Fenland Manuscripts*, London, 1974.

Scott (1879)
George Gilbert Scott, *Personal and Professional Recollections*, London, 1879.

Seymour (1967)
M.C. Seymour, *Mandeville's Travels*, Oxford, 1967.

Shaw (1823)
Henry Shaw, *A Series of Details of Gothic Architecture*, London, 1823.

Shaw (1837)
Henry Shaw, *Specimens of Ancient Furniture*, London, 1837.

Sirr (1883 & 1885)
H. Sirr, 'English Stall-Work, Canopies, and Rood-Screens of the Fifteenth Century', *Art Journal*, 1883, 325-29; and 1885, 145-48.

H. Smith (1921)
H. Clifford Smith, 'An English Fifteenth-century Panel', *The Antiquaries Jnl*, I, 1921, 300-02.

H. Smith (1923)
H. Clifford Smith, *Victoria and Albert Museum Department of Woodwork Catalogue of English Furniture and Woodwork, Vol.I, Gothic and Early Tudor*, London, 1923. Revised and reprinted 1929.

H. Smith (1925)
H. Clifford Smith, 'Some Mediaeval Ships', *Country Life*, May 9, 1925.

J. Smith (1969)
J.C.D. Smith, *Church Woodcarvings: A West Country Study*, Newton Abbot, 1969.

Stabb (1908-16)
John Stabb, *Some Old Devon Churches, their rood screens, pulpits, fonts etc.*, 3 Vols, London, 1908-16.

Steer (1973)
F.W. Steer, 'Misericords at New College, Oxford', Chichester, 1973

Street (1865)
G.E. Street, 'On English Woodwork in the Thirteenth and Fourteenth Centuries', *R.I.B.A. Jnl*, February 1865.

Stone (1972)
Lawrence Stone, *Sculpture in Britain: The Middle Ages*, London, 1972.

Swartout (1932)
R.E. Swartout, *The Monastic Craftsman*, Cambridge, 1932.

Symonds (1951)
R.W. Symonds, 'The Counter-Board and its use', *Connoisseur*, CXXVIII, Dec.1951, 169-75.

Symonds (1956)
R.W. Symonds, 'Furniture: Post Roman', from *A History of Technology*, ed.C. Singer *etc.*, Vol. II, Oxford, 1956.

Thomas (1903)
Archdeacon Thomas, 'Montgomeryshire Screens and Roodlofts', *Archaeologia Cambrensis*, 6th Ser., Vol.IV, Pt.II, 1903, 85-120.

Tracy (1985)
Charles Tracy, 'Dating the Misericords from the Thirteenth-Century Choir-Stalls at Exeter Cathedral', *B.A.A. Conference Transactions for Exeter Cathedral*, 1985, forthcoming.

Tracy (1986)
Charles Tracy, 'The early fourteenth-century choir-stalls at Exeter Cathedral', *The Burlington Magazine*, CXXVIII, February 1986, 99-103.

Tracy (1987)
Charles Tracy, *English Gothic Choir-Stalls. 1200-1400*, Woodbridge, 1987.

Tracy (forthcoming a)
Charles Tracy, 'The St David's Cathedral Bishop's Throne and its Relationship to contemporary fourteenth-century Furniture in England', *Arch.Camb.* (forthcoming).

Tracy (forthcoming b)
Charles Tracy, 'A boss from the Winchester Cathedral choir-stalls at the Victoria and Albert Museum', *Hampshire Field Club* (forthcoming).

Tredgold (1840)
T. Tredgold, *Elementary Principles of Carpentry*, 2nd Edn, with Appendix including additions by S.Smirke, J.Shaw, J.Glynn *et al.*, London, 1840.

Tucker (1846)
Charles Tucker, 'Notes on the bishop's palace, Exeter', *Arch.Jnl*, V, 1846, 224-25.

Vallance (1906)
Aymer Vallance, 'The Development of the Linen Panel', *Magazine of Fine Arts*, 1906, 212-22.

Vallance (1907)
Aymer Vallance, 'Mediaeval Rood-Lofts and Screens in Kent', from *Memorials of Old Kent*, London, 1907, 44-109.

Vallance (1907a)
Aymer Vallance, 'Roods, Screens, and Lofts in Derbyshire Churches', from *Memorials of Old Derbyshire*, London, 1907, 200-80.

Vallance (1909)
Aymer Vallance, 'The Pulpitum and Rood Screen in Monastic and Cathedral Churches', *St Paul's Ecclesiological Soc.Trans*, VI, 1909, 185-200.

Vallance (1909a)
Aymer Vallance, 'Roods, Screens, and Lofts in Middlesex', from *Memorials of Old Middlesex*, London, 1909, 85-101.

Vallance (1909b)
Aymer Vallance, 'Roods, Screens, and Lofts in Lancashire', from *Memorials of Old Lancashire*, 1909, 228-58.

Vallance (1911)
Aymer Vallance, 'Roods, Screens, and Lofts in Surrey', from *Memorials of Old Surrey*, London, 1911, 82-128.

Vallance (1912)
Aymer Vallance, 'Roods, Screens, and Lofts in Nottinghamshire', from *Memorials of Old Nottinghamshire*, London, 1912, 124-67.

Vallance (1917)
Aymer Vallance, 'The History of Roods, Screens, and Lofts in the East Riding', *Yorkshire Arch.Jnl*, XXIV, 1917, 109-185.

Vallance (1936)
Aymer Vallance, *English Church Screens*, London, 1936.

Vallance (1947)
Aymer Vallance, *Greater English Church Screens*, London, 1947.

V & A (1930)
Victoria and Albert Museum, *Catalogue of an Exhibition of English Medieval Art*, London, 1930.

V.C.H. (Lancashire)
W. Farrer & J. Brownbill (eds), V.C.H., *A History of Lancashire*, VIII, London, 1914.

Viollet-le-Duc (1858)
M. Viollet-le-Duc, *Dictionnaire Raisonné du Mobilier Français*, Paris, 1858.

Walker (1982)
Philip Walker, 'The Tools Available to the Mediaeval Woodworker', B.A.R. *Intl. Ser.*, 129, 1982, 349-56.

Warren (1935)
F. Warren, 'The Lost Panels of the Choir Stalls', *Winchester Cathedral Record*, 1935, 12-16.

Whittingham (1948)
A.B. Whittingham, 'The Stalls of Norwich Cathedral', *Friends of Norwich Cathedral, Annual Report*, 1948, 15-31

Whitworth (1976)
Whitworth Art Gallery, Manchester, *Medieval and Early Renaissance Treasures in the North West*, Exh.(15.1 – 28.2) Cat..

Wickenden (1881)
Canon Wickenden, 'The Choir Stalls of Lincoln Cathedral', *Arch. Jnl.*, XXXVIII, 1881, 42-61.

Wildridge (1879)
Thomas T. Wildridge, 'Misereres in Beverley Minster', Hull, 1879.

Wildridge (1889)
Thomas T. Wildridge, 'Misereres of Ripon Minster', Hull, 1889.

Windisch-Graetz (1982)
F. Windisch-Graetz, *Möbel Europas*, Munich, 1982.

C.G. Wilson (1976)
Corinne G. Wilson (Mrs Bennett), 'The Medieval Quire', *Winchester Cathedral Record*, 1976, 16-18.

Wolfgang (1911)
A. Wolfgang, 'Misericords in Lancashire and Cheshire Churches', *Hist.Soc of Lancs and Cheshire Trans*, LXIII, 1911, 79-87.

Wolfgang (1912)
A. Wolfgang, 'Ancient Screens in Cheshire and Lancashire Churches', *Hist.Soc of Lancs and Cheshire Trans*, LXIX, 1912, 20-42.

Woodforde (1951)
Christopher Woodforde, *The Stained Glass of New College, Oxford*, Oxford, 1951.

Wright (1848)
Thomas Wright, 'Carvings of the Stalls in Cathedral and Collegiate Churches', B.A.A.Jnl, IV, 1849, 203-216.

Wright (1865)
Thomas Wright, *History of Caricature in Literature and Art*, London, 1865.

INDEX OF PLACES

Note: Page numbers in Roman lower case, otherwise catalogue numbers referred to

Aberdeen, King's College, 50
Aberdeen, St Nicholas, 50
Aberdeen Cathedral, 50
Alderbury, Ivy Church House, Wilts, 315
Arundel, West Sussex, Fitzalan Chapel, xix
Athelington Church, Suffolk, 187-90
Balderton, St Giles, Notts, 215-17
Barningham Church, Suffolk, 184-85
Barningham Hall, Suffolk, 322
Barton Turf, Norfolk, 100-101
Bentley Church, Suffolk, 192
Berrynarbor Church, Devon, 1-4
Beverley, St Mary, Yorkshire, 57-58
Beverley Minster, Yorkshire, xix, xxv, 194
Bishops Lydeard, Somerset, 158
Blagdon Church, Somerset, 79-86
Bosham, Sussex, 296
Boston Church, Lincs, 57-58, 161
Bridwell, Devon, xxii
Brightleigh, Old Manor House, Devon, xxvii, 266
Bristol, St Mary Redcliffe, 67
Broadway, Somerset, 320, 324
Buckland-in-the-Moor Church, Devon, 102
Burton-on-Trent, Staffs, 239
Bury St Edmund's, St Mary, xx, 38-40, 160, 161, 240-42
Cambridge, King's College, 62-65
Carlisle Cathedral, xix
Chester Cathedral, xix, 67, 194
Chesterton Church, Norfolk, 161
Chichester Cathedral, xx, 17-23, 68, 93, 314
Chichester, St Mary's Hospital, xix
Clare, Church Farm, Suffolk, 247, 248, 255
Climping, Sussex, 296
Coggeshall, Paycocke's House, Suffolk, 247, 331-33
Cologne, St Maria im Kapitol, xx
Darlington Parish Church, Yorkshire, 68
Deddington Church, Oxfordshire, 51
Dodford Church, Northants, 45, 87
Duxford, Cambs, 257
Easby Abbey, Yorkshire, 238
East Brent Church, Somerset, 199
Ely Cathedral, xx, 13, 37, 89
Etchingham Church, East Sussex, xix
Ewelme Church, Oxon, 24-27
Exeter, Bishop's Palace, xxvii
Exeter Cathedral, xix, 1-4, 5-9, 37, 67, 102, 254
Exeter, St Thomas, xix
Farleigh Castle, Somerset, 43
Fawsley Church, Northants, 269
Feltwell Church, Norfolk, 161
Fressingfield Church, Suffolk, 164
Glastonbury Abbey, 1-4
Gloucester Cathedral, xix, 68, 89

Great Barton, Holy Innocents, Suffolk, 94
Great Bedwyn Church, Wilts, 298
Great Tew Church, Oxon, 195
Great Wenham Church, Suffolk, 192
Guildford, Surrey, Sutton Place, 154, 250, 256, 259, 262, 286, 318
Hadleigh, Suffolk, 245
Harlaxton Church, Lincs, 87
Hereford Cathedral, 37, 68, 252, 297
Hereford, All Saints, 297
Holme Church, Notts, 215-17
Honiton, Devon, 244
Ipswich, Suffolk, 249
King's Lynn, St Nicholas, xxvii, 69-72, 73-78, 158-183
Kingston, Somerset, 270
Lavenham, Suffolk, 252
Layer Marney, Essex, xx
Leigh Church, Wilts, 119
Lincoln Cathedral, xix, xxvii, 67, 87, 89, 96, 168, 194, 314
Linkinhorne Church, Cornwall, 200
Llanbadarn Church, Dyfed, 24-27
Llan-v-Bladwell Church, Shropshire, xxiv
London, Crosby Hall, xx, xxviii n.6
London, South Kensington Museum, xxi, xxii
London, Osterley Park, xxii
Long Melford Church, Suffolk, 38-40
Louth Church, Lincs, 42
Lower Docker Hall, Lancs, 268
Lustleigh, Devon, 246
Malmesbury Abbey, xxvii, 45, 87
Manchester Cathedral, xix, xxv, 194
March Church, Cambs, 38-40
Melbourne Church, Derbyshire, 46-47
Midhurst Church, Sussex, 296
Milton Ernest, Beds, 95
Muchelney Abbey, Somerset, 270
Nantwich Church, Cheshire, xix, 301
New York, Metropolitan Museum, 48
North Cheriton, Somerset, 233
Norwich, St Peter, Hungate, 157
Norwich, St John Maddermarket, 100-101
Norwich, St Gregory, 186
Norwich Cathedral, xix, 214
Occold Church, Suffolk, 87
Oswestry, Shropshire, Trinity Church, xxiv
Oxford, New College, xix, 301
Oxford, Magdalen College, xx, 277
Peterborough Cathedral, xix
Plymtree, Devon, 102
Prittlewell Church, Essex, 300
Rattlesden Church, Suffolk, 193
Ripon Minster, Yorks, xix, xxv, 194
Rochester Cathedral, xx
Rufford, Lancs, Old Rufford Hall, 73-78, xxvii

Saffron Walden Museum, Herts, 330
Salisbury Cathedral, xix, xx, 37, 68, 194
Sherborne Abbey, Dorset, 157
South Brent Church, Somerset, 199
Southwell Minster, 37
St Alban's Cathedral, xxvii, 172-3, 67
St Donat's Castle, Glamorgan, 315
St Ives Church, Cornwall, 201-202
St Katherine's Hospital-by-the-Tower, xix, xxvii, 67, 89
Stanton Harcourt Church, Oxon, 254
Steeple Aston Church, Oxon, 124
Stoke D'Abernon Church, Surrey, 296
Stonham Aspall Church, Suffolk, 162
Stowlangtoft Church, Suffolk, 162, 184-85
Stratford-on-Avon Church, xx
Syde, Gloucestershire, 316
Tatterford Church, Norfolk, 103
Thornham Parva Church, Suffolk, 254
Tilbrook Church, Cambs, 95
Tiverton Church, Devon, 158
Trunch Church, Norfolk, 330
Ufford Church, Suffolk, 161
Ugborough Church, Devon, 102
Walpole St Peter Church, Norfolk. 100-101, 160
Wells Cathedral, xxvii, 1-4, 5-9, 13, 66, 89, 194
Wensley Church, Yorkshire, 238
West Stow Church, Suffolk, 104
Westminster, Royal Architectural Museum, xxi, 10-12, 28, 45, 57-58, 65-68, 69-72, 73-78, 89, 120, 121, 128-30, 132, 136, 158-183, 162, 163, 169, 177, 194, 260, 272-76, 278,
Westminster Abbey, Henry V Chantry, 161, 234-35
Westminster Abbey, xx, 45
Westminster Abbey, Henry VII Chapel, xx
Westminster Palace, St Stephen's Chapel, 67, 89
Whalley Abbey, Lancs, 149
Wheathampstead Church, Herts, 236
Wiggenhall St German's Church, Norfolk, 161, 164, 168
Wilby Church, Suffolk, 187-90
Winchester Cathedral, xix, xxvii, 17-23, 68, 90, 91, 93, 157
Windsor, St George's Chapel, xix, xxvi, 89, 92, 157, 161
Woodspring Priory, Somerset, 79-86
Worle Church, Somerset, 79-86
Wraxall Church, Avon, 269
Wymondham Church, Norfolk, 49
York Minster, 314
York, All Saints, 62-65
Ypres Museum, Belgium, 300
Zeal Monachorum Church, Devon, 109